RIVER ON THE RAMPAGE

DOUBLEDAY & COMPANY, INC., GARDEN CITY, N.Y., 1953

RIVER ON THE RAMPAGE

BY KENNETH S. DAVIS

A small portion of "A Rage of Waters," Section 2 of Part I of this book, was originally printed in the New York *Times Magazine*, September 2, 1951, as part of an article entitled "Kansas Can't Forget THE Flood." It is reprinted here with the permission of the *Times*.

The quotation on page 9 is from "The Dry Salvages," in *Four Quartets*, copyright, 1943, by T. S. Eliot; reprinted by permission of Harcourt, Brace and Company, Inc., and Faber and Faber Limited.

The quotation from the article by Leslie A. Miller is reprinted by permission of Mr. Miller.

Library of Congress Catalog Card Number 53–5298

DESIGNED BY DIANA KLEMIN

For Russell Lord, pioneer in the literature of conservation

When Achelous, the river-god, fought Hercules for the hand of Dejanira, fairest of maidens, he was overcome. He then transformed himself into a snake and was again overcome. Finally he transformed himself into a bull, and yet again was he overcome and a horn torn from his head by the ruthless hand of Hercules. Seized by the naiads, this horn was consecrated and filled with flowers and adopted by the goddess of plenty, who called it "Cornucopia."

According to Bulfinch, the ancients explained this myth by saying that Achelous was a river that overflowed its bank in seasons of rain. Its snake form was indicated by its winding, its form of a bull by the roaring noise it made in its course. In flood the river formed another channel, and thus its head was horned. With embankments and canals Hercules prevented such floods and was therefore said to have vanquished the river-god and cut off his horn. The lands formerly flooded now became very fertile, and this is meant by the horn of plenty.

T. S. ELIOT, *The Dry Salvages*, in FOUR QUARTETS

I do not know much about gods; but I think that the river
Is a strong brown god—sullen, untamed and intractable,
Patient to some degree, at first recognised as a frontier;
Useful, untrustworthy, as a conveyor of commerce;
Then only a problem confronting the builder of bridges.

The problem once solved, the brown god is almost forgotten
By the dwellers in cities—ever, however, implacable,
Keeping his seasons and rages, destroyer, reminder
Of what men choose to forget. Unhonoured, unpropitiated
By worshippers of the machine, but waiting, watching and
   waiting.

Acknowledgments   Several busy people reviewed the manuscript of this book, giving the author their suggestions and criticisms. None of them is responsible for such errors of fact or interpretation as the book may yet contain, but each has helped the author avoid mistakes he would otherwise have made, and to each he is profoundly grateful.

Among these readers were Harold J. Swan, head of the current information section of the U. S. Soil Conservation Service regional office, Lincoln, Nebraska; Gladwin E. Young, field representative of the Secretary of Agriculture, Lincoln, Nebraska; C. D. Sanders, head of the flood-control section of the U. S. Soil Conservation Service regional office, Lincoln, Nebraska; L. R. Combs, deputy chief of the Division of Information, U. S. Soil Conservation Service, Washington, D.C.; Ralph Porges, sanitary engineer, Division of Water Pollution Control of the Missouri Drainage Basin, Public Health Service, Kansas City, Mo.; Dwight F. Metzler, director of the Division of Sanitation, Kansas State Board of Health, Lawrence, Kansas; Glenn D. Stockwell, chairman of the Blue Valley Study Association, Randolph, Kansas; and Russell Lord, editor of *The Land* and frequently employed as special consultant by Federal agencies working in the field of soil and water conservation.

K.S.D.

Foreword   Some years ago, when Mortimer Adler's *How to Think about War and Peace* was published, a number of reviewers took exception to the title, claiming that it indicated intellectual arrogance of the most deplorable kind. It is therefore with some trepidation that I confess that this little book has borne in my mind the working title of *How to Think about a River*. I hasten to add that I would not presume to tell *you* how to think about a river or anything else, or to imply that you don't do so better than I'll ever learn to do. My intention has been merely to reveal as interestingly as I can my own effort to learn about a river whose moods profoundly affect the community in which I live, and to think about it accurately. My hope is that this effort of mine will stimulate a similar effort by you. For whatever the deficiencies of my book, the problems with which it deals are of major importance to all of us. Nor are they problems of a merely physical or technical nature: as I see them, they are also problems in sociology, in economics, in politics, in education, in philosophy.

Because the river is a *flowing* reality, one aspect of it is continuously merging with another. This makes it difficult to organize into a systematic treatise one's thoughts about it—and I confess I've made no serious effort to do so. I've been content with a series of related essays in which first one, then another aspect of river is considered, and in which those problems which most interest me—probably because I have more information about them than

I do about others—have received an emphasis disproportionate, no doubt, to their importance in the total scheme of things. This doesn't worry me. What *does* worry me a little is the difficulty of "placing" the book in any clearly defined category. Here are pictures of landscape, glimpses of history, expositions of technical problems, excursions into politics, criticisms of education, even a moment or two of metaphysical speculation—in short, a grab bag of a book. I'd hoped this might make a kind of "funferal," to use Joyce's description of *Finnegans Wake*. But I'm afraid it will merely irritate professional reviewers and the editors of book sections—an overworked crew who naturally resent oddities for which they cannot find convenient labels. It is a risk I must run.

One last word.

Though I've written in terms of the Kansas River Basin, the conclusions reached must, if they are valid, have a very general application. As David Lilienthal said in his book *TVA, Democracy on the March*, "All this could have happened in almost any one of a thousand other valleys where the rivers run from the hills to the sea . . . [for] in a thousand valleys in America and the world over there are fields that need to be made strong and productive, land steep and rugged, land flat as a man's hand. . . ." There are also droughts, and floods, and a complex of competing interests focused on the river, requiring that we approach the valley with whole minds and in an honest spirit.

K.S.D.

Polluted Waters IV

The Evolution of River Planning V

Of Education and the River VI

Variations on a Theme of Water

1

The Eerie Light of Dusty Death   The spring of 1950 was dry in Kansas as it was through all the Southwest, and on the fifth of May we had a "duster" reminiscent of the early 1930s here in Manhattan, Kansas, where I live.

On the evening of the fourth the sun went down behind orange clouds, and in its last light could be seen a gray wall leaning over us out of the southwest. At sunset the east was more vividly colored than the west. Far down the valley of the Kaw (or Kansas) River, the edge of our world was a deep purple above which streamed banners of amethyst, primrose, ocher, a crimson as vivid as the cardinal in our osage orange tree, a yellow as bright as the Baltimore oriole who that year flitted through our wild plum thicket. Then, quite abruptly, the streaming colors of the east seemed to run together into a muddy amber. Day died into night without the usual graduation: a shrieking wind blew the light out.

All night long the wind cried across the hill on which our house stands. We listened to gusty sighs which, sustained for a time, always slurred up the scale of sound into shrieks of utter desolation, then died again into a low steady whine. The darkness had a bitter taste. It seemed to congeal in fine grit upon one's skin; it was acrid in the nostrils. And within its turbulence was no restful sleep. We dozed fitfully and awoke in the morning weary of the wind and of the smell of dusty death, eyes smarting, the throat already raw, nerves tightened to an irritable pitch; and the world we saw from our Kansas window was, in early light, a silver-gray.

The first light spread evenly over all the sky, from east to west. The morning sun was a silver dollar above the concrete "K" and "S" (for Kansas State College) on Prospect Hill beyond the eastern edge of our town. But before long the sky had turned the color of mud, the sun had disappeared, and the high ceiling of fine dust out of Texas and Oklahoma and western Kansas was but an invisible top to a thick brownish-gray pall sweeping in from Ashland Bottoms and Hunters Island immediately south and west of our town. Even then the dreary light was evenly spread, lacking any apparent source, as though each tiny particle of dust had been struck off a dying sun and was still feebly glowing.

We lived through that weary day in a shrinking world. The hills beyond the town were gone by noon. An hour later the college buildings a quarter of a mile east of us were fading, dissolving into dust. In late afternoon we could barely see the vacant lot, a block away, where we'd gardened the year before—and only the headlights of cars were visible on U.S. 24, one hundred yards from our hill. The world was as eerie as it was narrow. We had a sense of entombment and slow suffocation in some ghastly attenuated earth through which pale glowworms crawled: the silver-green lights of cars, of street lamps, of house windows: and across our tomb the wind grieved endlessly in long dry dusty wails, a grief with malevolence in it. . . .

The dim sourceless light defined familiar objects in strange ways.

Once that afternoon I looked up from my study desk and saw snow upon the plum thicket outside my window. "Only it can't be snow," I told myself. Every naked branch, every twig, was etched in a silver that looked substantial, as though it had been driven upon the wind and clung now, in white plating, to the bark. When I looked out through the other window, to the south, I saw that same silver stuff encrusting telephone wires and the darkened edges of a limestone wall. "But it's too warm for snow," I told myself.

So I went out into the shrieking, dusty wind and felt with my finger upon the thicket bark, and there was no substance on it save dust. The silver was all a trick of light, a sun drowned in dust, its beams dispersed in ten billion particles—the light of death and disintegration.

On that day I was reminded that this valley of the Kaw, like most of the Missouri Valley, is somewhat analogous in terms of climate and natural soil cover to vast areas of central Asia and the Middle East, areas which just a second ago by geologic time were richly agricultural, dotted by mighty cities that are empty ruins now upon a dead and empty land. I was reminded that the Sahara, having drowned in sand what was once the granary of Rome, now marched southward upon arable land at the rate of a half mile and more a year. I remembered how this very land before my eyes had looked in the early 1930s—the Flint Hills burnt brown by the blazing sun—when drought year succeeded drought year and dust from barren farms across the southern High Plains made a twilight of high noon in our town, not just once but many times.

Even on that day of the worst "duster" in years, I would not have suggested that Kansas was on the verge of becoming a Sahara, of course—but certainly I thought the dust bowl might be coming again. I looked toward the summer with apprehension.

2

A Rage of Waters   Drought didn't come in 1950, however. Instead the rains came at almost precisely the right times throughout the summer, so that we had bumper crops and the Kansas landscape was as lushly green and lovely as I've ever seen it. The rain-washed air was cool: we had none of those days of debilitating heat which are sometimes deemed typically Kansan in July and August.

The following winter was a trifle dry, but when spring came again it brought no return of "dusters." Instead it brought the heaviest, most prolonged rains in all our history. . . .

By mid-July of '51—with the year but half gone—every annual rainfall record was broken. In Manhattan, where the annual precipitation averages 30 inches, 21–38 inches fell in May and June alone. And what happened in Manhattan happened over most of the drainage areas of the Republican and Smoky Hill, whose junction 15 miles west of Manhattan forms the Kaw. It happened, too, all up the valley of the Blue, which flows into the Kaw at Manhattan and increases our town's flood hazards. We watched with growing dismay through those two months as flood crest followed flood crest until, on June 29, a peak nearly 10½ feet above flood stage was reached by the Kaw here. Muddy waters swirled over the eastern portion of the town, covering half the business district, and over lowlands all the way to Kansas City, whose bottomland industrial area huddled nervously behind levees and flood walls. These last were not topped nor breached. Slowly, while the Missouri flooded, the Kaw went down until, by July 9, it was almost within its banks again for the first time since early June. Sighing with disgust and relief, eastern Kansas began to count its losses and dig out.

But the ultimate water torture was yet to come. On July 9 rain again fell in torrents all across the anguished watershed. As much as seven inches fell within twenty-four hours some places; that much fell in thirty-six hours in Manhattan. By the evening of July 10 the Republican, the Smoky Hill, the Kaw, the Blue—all were raging out of their banks again, angrier than ever. And the end was not yet! The climactic deluge came that night, a prolonged cloud-burst measuring one and a half to six inches over the entire Kaw-Blue watershed. In less than two and a half months much of the basin had received four to six inches more rain than normally falls in an entire year. Abruptly Manhattan, a town of 17,000, found itself the gathering point for the greatest of all Kaw floods since 1844 while downstream areas braced themselves. When the Kaw finally crested here on Black Friday the thirteenth it was 17 feet over flood stage and its angry waters tore through the entire downtown business district, swirled across more than 200 blocks of residential district. Nearly 2,000 refugees, some of them forced from their homes with fifteen minutes' leeway, others hazardously rescued by boat or helicopter, were being housed and fed on the Kansas State College campus; hundreds more were jammed into private housing in the dry areas. Most city power and all city phones were knocked out, and helpless, miserable people huddled around radio loud-speakers (operated from a now-overloaded college power plant) for news of what to most of them was unmitigated catastrophe. One may easily insure his property against fire and theft, tornado and explosion, but it is impossible, practically speaking, to buy private insurance against floods. . . .

Downstream the story was repeated, and in crescendo.

At Topeka a levee protecting the northern part of the city broke: portions of North Topeka were swept clear of buildings by the immense torrent, four bridges were destroyed, and an oil fire raged. North of Lawrence, where the flood went high enough some places to hang debris on telephone lines, there was utter ruin. At Kansas City, where the great stockyards, packing plants, and much other industry lie on a bottomland triangle formed by the confluence of the Kaw and Missouri, the Army Engineers had built levees and flood walls 35 feet high—yet water came over those walls, then ripped through some of them and came in waves 10 to 20 feet high upon streets and buildings. Some areas were transformed within two hours from busy sections of a city to a debris-piled lake whose waters were 14 feet deep. Union Station, one of the greatest traffic centers in America, where 150 trains arrive and depart daily, was paralyzed, and in the flood were caught 10,000 empty freight cars, 2,500 loaded ones, and hundreds of locomotives. Torn from their foundations, drifting on the surface of turbulent waters, were huge oil-storage tanks. One containing 6,000 gallons struck a fallen high-tension electric line, exploded, covered the water with flaming oil, and set fire to two other tanks containing 800,000 gallons of Diesel fuel. The worst fire in Kansas City's history followed; for five days it raged, destroying seven solid blocks of buildings with an estimated value of $10,000,000. Absorbed into the Missouri, which fortunately was not itself in high water north of Kansas City, the flood eastward to St. Louis was diminished. Even so a dozen Missouri towns and thousands of acres of farmland felt the waters' crushing weight, and at St. Louis the waterfront suffered $4,000,000 of damage.

Along 750 miles from the headwaters of the Kaw to the Missouri's mouth, 44 people were killed. (In Manhattan two died: an Army captain, his heart overstrained by excitement and physical effort, fainted into rising water before Riley County's courthouse and drowned; in the southeastern corner of town an old stone house collapsed into the rampant river, crushing a 60-year-old woman.) And the wonder is that the death list was not longer. More than a half million people were driven from their homes, 2,000,000 acres were flooded, 45,000 houses were damaged or destroyed, and 17 major bridges, some of them weighted with locomotives in a vain effort to hold them, were washed away. By October, estimates of the total cost had mounted as high as $2,500,000,000—making this by far the costliest flood in the nation's history. In Manhattan alone the cost was estimated at more than $20,000,000, well over a thousand dollars for every man, woman, and child in town. . . .

Many weeks after the flood went down, the valley of the Kaw remained a stinking, dreary mess. Never will I personally forget the drive I took on U.S. 40 westward from Kansas City in late August of '51, six weeks after the river had crept sullenly back into its banks. The landscape had long been familiar to me, yet I found it now strange. All up the valley of the Kaw once-green bottoms were transformed into gray dune-streaked wastes dotted with fetid pools, streaked with muddy rivulets, heaped with all manner of debris, including the wrecks of houses and barns. In the worst places the stink of death still mingled with that thick acrid dust which, of all the various forms of the flood's aftermath, was common denominator. Wherever men moved, or the wind, powdered silt born of recent liquid mud drifted high into the warm late-summer air and hung there, a yellowish-gray shroud over a soil dead of drowning. At Lawrence, Perry, North Topeka —in all the stricken towns—the dust pall was particularly heavy. Through its gloom weary, sweaty men daily witnessed new havoc wrought by an earth that shuddered in anguish, then sank in despair as subterranean lakes receded and hidden caverns collapsed. In North Topeka, when I drove through, houses were still sinking into secret mud, some of them dropping down to their eaves.

As I drove into Manhattan from the east, the first sight of my home town's segment of flood havoc was a half mile east of the

bridge across the Blue, whose outlet into the Kaw, once adjacent
to Manhattan, was shifted two miles eastward by the great flood
of 1903. There most of a once-lovely tree nursery had become a
waste of brown, dead, mud-coated evergreens. And from there on
in I witnessed scenes of utter desolation. To the right a field air-
port had become a Dali-like landscape of bare caked mud from
which protruded the dead body of an uprooted tree with a tire
casing draped over one bough. Beside the tree stood the forlorn
wreck of a plane and beyond that a wind-sock pole tipped at a
crazy angle. To the left extra-large work crews were restoring the
wrecked Union Pacific roadbed, bulldozers were scraping tons of
silt from the highway's edge, and on the other side of the railway
embankment the Kaw now seemed a wholly Western river:
shallow, shoal-strewn, meandering, and apparently scores of yards
wider than it had formerly been.

At the eastern edge of the town, beside railroad tracks that had
been fantastically torn up and heaped with debris two weeks before, was a red brick packing-company building with a gaping
hole in one corner, its second story shored up with timbers. In
front of it a section of the street had dropped down, and in the
30-foot-deep hole were lost a passenger car and two trucks. One
truck was being left there as part of the eventual fill. All down
Poyntz Avenue, main street of the town, scenes of wreckage
multiplied: glass fronts of buildings shattered, plate-glass windows gone, sidewalks buckled, a building wholly collapsed on a
side street, a 15-foot cave-in of an alley beside City Hall, heaps
of stinking debris before stores, and everywhere the monotone
of caked mud and the dust pall born of it, streaked now and
then by rivers of still-liquid mud being pumped from basements.
Here and there signs proclaimed flood sales, and customers, most
of them flood victims themselves, bought for salvage prices
damaged goods piled up in ruined rooms.

West of the business district the woeful tale continued. Beside the Congregational Church the pastor and members of his congregation heaved pails of muck and broken plaster from the wrecked basement. Into the high school yard volunteer workers carried muddy mounds of books, of broken furniture—and on parkings before houses in each of more than twelve blocks up Poyntz, ruined household possessions were heaped up, and this despite the thousands of tons of debris that had already been hauled away. A third of all Manhattan's families—6,000 people—had been driven from their homes by the disaster, and each of them returned to heartbreaking, backbreaking labor. . . .

Nor will I ever forget the rare sense of community which developed in Manhattan during those weeks of severest trial—as it does in almost any town under the impact of disaster. Sharing one another's misfortunes, helping those less fortunate than ourselves, working together to the utmost limits of our strength, we came to know one another in new ways and to measure ourselves by a standard of values different from that usually employed in our town. People who'd been strangers became, for the time being, friends; people who'd believed they disliked one another came often to respect and even enjoy one another; and the mild enmities which had divided College from Downtown were, again for the time being, completely dissolved. It was the college, with its dry hill campus and with its staff (who lived for the most part in unflooded areas), with its technical facilities and material resources—it was the college that had "saved" the town on Black Friday, and many a businessman was heard to say that never again would he criticize "that college crowd."

A large generosity of purpose was dominant during those weeks. There was a sincere commitment to the general welfare and a consequent emphasis on the means and values of cooperation as opposed to self-centered competitive individualism. Many of my good neighbors here are men whose lifelong belief, often and vehemently stated, is that private profit is the only possible incentive for creative enterprise and the sole valid measure of its value. Yet during the flood I heard such men express the hope that our town would retain, as a permanent asset, the "spirit" which at that moment prevailed.

Often it expressed itself, this sense of solidarity, in a grim, wry humor, defying hostile fate. I remember that in the devastated business area the head of a plaster manikin was mounted on a parking meter, a large stencil for "Sympathy" hung round her neck. In a gutted alley another plaster manikin, feet clad in rubbers, thrust its bare legs from a pile of dirt bearing a sign reading, "Here Lies the Remains of D. C. Wesche"—Wesche being our sorely tried city engineer. I remember, too, how I followed on a hot afternoon one of the trucks piled high with flood debris out to the little farm of Curtis Hassebroek a half mile southeast of town, there to find another evidence of a subordination of individual to community welfare, and of the lyric enrichment of the individual life that can come from it. One of the first crucial problems faced by city officials as the water went down was location of a new city dump for the unbelievable mess of the flood: the old one was under ten feet of water. And the problem would have been hard indeed to solve had not Hassebroek offered a huge ravine on his place in the hills. In the weeks that followed trucks of mud and ruined possessions deposited their loads there at the rate of one a minute, twenty hours a day.

"Folks say I'm crazy to let this stuff on my place," he told me, "and some of my neighbors complain. But Manhattan had a tough problem—and I'm *for* Manhattan, strong as horseradish!"

He gestured toward the muck heap bordering the highway past his land.

"When this is over I'm going to bulldoze topsoil over that mess," he added earnestly. "Then I'm going to plant flowers there —just to show folks how good things can grow from bad."

Across Poyntz Avenue at what was normally our busiest intersection a banner was stretched in those days by our Chamber of Commerce. It proclaimed that "Manhattan Will Rise Again!" (to which cynics replied, "So Will the Kaw!"), and of course the prophecy came true (as the cynical one was bound to do sooner or later). Often we speak of the "miracle" of a city's recovery from fire, or flood, or earthquake—but really this is the usual thing: men in a burst of co-operative effort generally restore, and speedily, their material wealth after such disasters, though at an uncounted cost in natural resources. Equally common, alas, is the departure of the co-operative spirit as prosperity returns. To a large extent this happened in my home town. A visitor driving up Poyntz Avenue in the summer of '52 would never have guessed from what he saw that the town had recently come close to being wiped out: if he involved himself intimately in the town he might have found it difficult to believe in the selfless generosity which, twelve months before, had been our general mood. We were again "rugged individualists," and even as regards flood-control issues most of us took our stands according to our immediate selfish interests rather than with a concern for the general good.

The Kaw flowed on, "unhonoured, unpropitiated by worshippers of the machine, but waiting, watching and waiting."

3

From Flood to Drought But though the town lost almost all visible memory of the flood within twelve months after the waters went down, the countryside did not. The marks of disaster were everywhere about me when I went again down to the river on an August day in '52.

Through a hot bright morning I drove alone southwestward from our town along U.S. 40, past rows of new frame houses spread across hills that only twenty years ago, and despite their nearness to the town, were yet wild and lonely, until I came to the Sky-Vue Drive-in Theater where, according to the sign, a "Double-Feature Corn Show" was playing. There I turned southward onto a dusty road which hugged a wave of lime-ridged earth rising 200 feet above the valley floor and curved round the western edge of Moehlmann Bottoms. Seen from that road, the Bottoms were now a ruined landscape. Dunes of sand sustained but meager patches of weeds across hundreds of once-fertile acres, and there was a chaos of gully and raw cliff and fantastic low-lying earthen mesas, heaped with driftwood, where the river last year had come close to carving a new channel.

I passed what was once a living community, a grove of fine trees whose leafy tops had merged to form a single unbroken cover in summertime and upon whose boughs birds had nested thickly, generation after generation, for a half century and more. The trees were all dead now. They were drowned through weeks of standing in fetid water—and in their death was no community. Each pale corpse stood up alone, withdrawn from its neighbors, and it but narrowly spread its boughs, now naked and desolate, above a weedy wasteland. I passed a large stone house. Surrounding it once was a level, beautifully kept lawn of bluegrass; surrounding it now were rolling waves of sand, heaped in odd corners with debris, while streaming tufts of dead grass in the elm boughs above it marked how swift and high was the water here. I rounded a curve, climbing slightly, and came abruptly to the end of the road. Here I would formerly have crossed first the Union Pacific railroad track, then a bridge across the Kaw into bottoms called Ashland that spread, flat and rich, from river to Flint Hills ridge miles to the south. The bridge was now destroyed. One of its three spans had been washed entirely away the year before, as was the heavy plank flooring of the other two.

A car was parked against the wooden fence where the road

was cut off. I parked my own beside it and walked out to the edge of the riverbank. I sat there upon one of the great blocks of limestone with which the Union Pacific seeks to hold its right of way against the stream's erosion—and as I looked down upon the brown shoal-divided waters, the river so blandly innocent and shrunken within its banks, the rock revetment seemed useless to the point of absurdity. The swollen rage of this same river last year seemed utterly impossible. The rains of last year seemed impossible too.

Above me arched a blazing sky from which no moisture of consequence had come since early June (great cracks had opened in earth which last year was mud for weeks on end, while the sweet corn in my garden was stunted and barren of ears). I could not then know that the drought of '52 had barely begun: through the remainder of August there would be no rain, nor in September, October, and through most of November. Not in eighty years had Kansas had so little moisture for so long a period, the Weather Bureau would tell us, while crop specialists from the college found prospects for the wheat crop of '53 to be poor indeed. But even on that August morning the drought seemed severe enough. Far across the Ashland Bottoms I saw Flint Hills, which were bleached a pale green, with patches of burnt brown upon their slopes—and I knew that white-faced cattle on those far pastures were not as fat as they might be at that time of year because of the shortage of succulent grasses. Then, just across the river, I noticed the air shuddering in heat prostration above a narrow desert of sand where formerly grew a jungle of willow and cottonwood. Somehow that new-made stretch of wasteland seemed a signature upon all I'd seen that morning. It was a symptom of the sickness of a thousand river valleys, evoking a mood which must dominate my working hours for weeks to come.

A whirring sound, below and to the left, startled me. Looking down quickly, I saw, relieved, that the driver of the car beside which I'd parked my own was fishing there with rod and reel. He sat upon a limestone slab, leaning his back against the trunk of an uprooted elm: lazily he cast his line into the sluggish stream. Perhaps he practiced casting in preparation for a vacation to the north or west, for certainly he fished that day (alas) in warm and muddy waters and had no luck while I watched him.

Afterward I climbed the limestone hill whose lower slope came gently down to the river before the railroad cut a path across it. Above the railroad cut the slope was steep and I grasped clumps of sumac in order to pull myself upward. Then, panting and sweating, I stood upon the crest, surveying in panorama the flat, hot, sand-streaked land curving around me from Manhattan westward toward Fort Riley, remarking that barely a year ago all those thirsty acres were covered by water, from bluff to bluff, as Indians a hundred years ago had warned they would be. How striking was the contrast! It was as though nature through those last sixteen months, after a dozen grateful growing seasons, were bent on reminding us as forcefully as possible that water remains the major physical problem throughout our Kansas Basin, and throughout the whole of the Missouri Valley, whose boundaries enclose a sixth of all the nation's land.

Water!

We can have too much or too little of it in any year at almost any place from St. Louis and the Missouri's mouth to western Montana's mountains and those prairie rims of southern Alberta and Saskatchewan where lie the farthest reaches of the vast watershed.

Portrait of a Watershed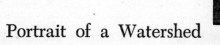

The Watershed as Landscape **1**

The Watershed as Process **2**

The Watershed in History **3**

1

The Watershed as Landscape   We speak of the "basin" of the Kansas River, and the word is not inaccurate as description. The basin, however, is of peculiar shape. Were the sky which covers it a solid substance whose horizons coincided with the highest ridges of watershed, the basin would be transformed into a vast pinch bottle some 500 miles long and, viewed from above, 190 miles wide at its widest portions, gently sloping from west to east and tapering abruptly at its eastern end to form a narrow bottleneck. This neck would have as its eastern terminus a relatively tiny opening, only a few hundred yards wide—the width of the Kansas River itself as it flows into the Missouri.

The basin as a whole contains approximately 60,060 square miles. It also contains both the geodetic and geographic centers of the United States: the former, from which longitude and latitude are calculated, is in Osborne County, Kansas, and the latter is in Smith County, a few miles to the north. Roughly 16 per cent of the total area lies in Colorado, 28 per cent lies in Nebraska, and the remaining 56 per cent is in Kansas. Actually the main stem of the Kaw (the name by which the river is known to all who live in its valley) flows only 169 tortuous miles, or about 135 in a straight east-and-west line, from Junction City, Kansas, to Kansas City. It drains but 5,554 square miles, barely 9 per cent of the total basin area. Its main tributary, the Blue, flowing down from the north through a particularly lovely valley and meeting the Kaw at Manhattan, 120 miles west of Kansas City, drains a much larger area—some 9,600 square miles in east central Nebraska and Kansas.

Larger still are the sub-basins of the Republican and Smoky Hill rivers, which flow together at Junction City (so named for that reason) to form the Kaw. The Republican's drainage area contains nearly 25,000 square miles, the bulk of it in western Nebraska, western Kansas, and eastern Colorado. The Smoky Hill, with its two main tributaries, the Solomon and the Saline, drains approximately 20,000 square miles. A tiny portion of this area lies in eastern Colorado. The rest lies in central and western Kansas.

Thus the general composition of the Kansas River Basin. No spectacular ridges, no grandeurs of mountain peak separate it from the North Platte and Nemaha Basin to the north and northwest, nor from the Arkansas and Marais des Cygnes Basin in the south and southwest. Only by careful survey have civil engineers determined the precise edge of the bowl, the ultimate contour line dividing rain between this basin and its immediate neighbors. Nevertheless, one climbs a mountain height as one travels from the eastern to the western limits. The elevation at Kansas City is some 770 feet; the elevation in Lincoln County, Colorado, where the basin has its farthest western tip, is around 4,300 feet; and the difference of more than 3,500 feet is about equal to the climb from base to top of a typical 14,000-foot peak in the Colorado Rockies.

One also, traveling from east to west, moves in steady and swift progression from a land of sufficient rain through a land of uncertain rain into a land where rain, in an average year, is a rare event and ground water a precious commodity. At Kansas City, the average annual precipitation is between 35 and 40 inches a year. At Junction City, 145 miles to the west, it averages 30 inches a year. At the 99th meridian, halfway across the basin, it averages 25 inches. One hundred miles beyond that, it averages only 20 inches; and in the far western reaches of the basin the country approaches desert conditions, the rainfall averaging but little more than 15 inches—which means a good deal less than that falls in many years. Indeed, this deficiency of rain in the west would render inaccurate an assertion that the Republican River actually drains 25,000 square miles. That area is, as we've said, encompassed in the watershed, but some thousands of these miles are marked on drainage maps as "non-contributing areas"; no significant amount of runoff water normally flows from them into the central streams.

To those concerned with stream pollution, soil conservation, and flood control, the manner in which the rain comes to this land is as important as the amount which comes. Other areas, having no more moisture than Kansas and Nebraska in an average year, may escape the droughts which plague this region—and the frequent floods. They may do so because their rains are more evenly distributed through the seasons, are more frequent and less furious. In the Kansas Basin, and particularly in the middle and western portions, much of the rain which falls does so as a liquid lash across the land. Huge drops strike all naked earth so violently as to shatter its surface into dust-sized particles. These, caught up and held in suspension, quickly clog the earth pores and prevent the absorption which would otherwise occur. "Puddling," this is called. Its consequence is a high proportion of runoff, swelling the streams with moisture, and increasing their turbidity with soil which is badly needed on the uplands.

Differences in prevailing wind velocities between the eastern and western portions are almost as great as the differences in rainfall. In the eastern portion, winds are not perceptibly higher than they are in eastern United States as a whole, but the western portion is among the windiest of all inland sections of the continent. A stranger to the High Plains is always impressed and often dismayed by the seemingly endless storm of wind he encounters there. He has to lean against it as he walks, and squint his eyes against its blast. He hears it sobbing around the corners of houses and moaning through the scant-leaved boughs of rare and stunted trees. In winter he sees it defined in clouds of dust or snow across the fields. Dust storms are common in those seasons when the cultivated earth is bare of vegetation, and their severity in years of extreme drought is both spectacular and terrifying.

The normal annual mean temperature throughout the basin approximates 50 degrees F., with a winter mean of around 25 degrees and a summer one of around 75 degrees. This tells one little, however, of actual temperatures as residents experience them, for the basin lies in the path of air currents flowing north from the Tropics and south from the Arctic, and the temperatures in any given locality have wide and sometimes swift variations. In an average year the range between summer and winter temperatures is around 100 degrees, but in any one year it may be much greater. In Manhattan, Kansas, for instance, the temperature range in a recent year was some 140 degrees—from around 32 degrees below zero to nearly 110 degrees above—and for the basin as a whole (though not in the same year) the range has been 165 degrees: from 47 below zero to 118 above. In general, the western tablelands are somewhat cooler than the lower lands to the east. A summer evening on the High Plains is normally pleasant, even when the preceding afternoon is blazing hot, and visitors from more humid areas are likely to speak gratefully of sleeping under blankets at night despite a temperature reading at 3 P.M. of 100 degrees.

It should be added that the wide difference between temperature extremes does not deny to the region its fair quota, if not more, of pleasant, healthful weather. The long springs and autumns are lovely seasons, and there have been years in Kansas (many of the 1940s were such years) in which the countryside remained as lushly green all summer long as rural New England, and the thermometer seldom registered more than 85 degrees. Few if any areas of equivalent rainfall have a higher percentage of cloud-free days: the relative humidity on the average is low, and fogs or mists are very rare. This means, of course, a high evaporation rate—a factor of importance to the natural water economy, and hence to river-development plans, across the plains. . . .

In terms of climate, then, the basin may be roughly divided into three areas, each occupying a third of the distance from the mouth of the Kaw to those remote western highlands where the Arikaree, famed in Indian wars, has its sources. And these climatic conditions coincide, though again very roughly, with three quite different kinds of landscape—differing in shape, in color, in natural vegetation.

The *eastern* landscape is one of stream and river flood plains, flat and rich and varying in width from a mile or so to 15 or 20, bounded by limestone hills rising 200 to 500 feet above the valley floors. Here corn is a principal crop and a widely diversified farming is practiced; here, too, are found the largest towns of the region. Trees grow tall and thick along the rivers and in farm wood lots: village streets lie in the deep shade of high-arched, dense-leaved branches. The rock-ridged hills themselves—shaggy with tall grasses where ungrazed, bearing few trees on their sides and none on their crests—become the dominant feature of the Kansas landscape a few miles west of Topeka. These are the Flint Hills, components of the bluestem belt, whose vistas of surpassing loveliness invariably surprise strangers accustomed, as most of them are, to thinking of this whole region as a flat, monotonous plain. The hills form a belt some 30 to 40 miles wide, extending south from beyond the Nebraska line into Oklahoma, and to them are shipped for summer grazing a third of a million cattle each year, most of them from the American Southwest but some of them from Mexico. It is a unique grazing area. The bluestems and their associated grasses are so lush in their growth, and so nourishing, that many cattle are actually finished on them, selling grass-fat and profitably on the Kansas City and Omaha markets. The prevailing color note through the whole of this land-scape in summer is a deep blue-green.

This bleaches toward a yellow-green as one moves into the *middle* landscape, beyond the bluestem belt. This portion of the basin bulges 83 miles into Nebraska and 106 miles into Kansas and its scenery is less impressive than the Flint Hills. The valleys are wider, the hills lower, and of natural vegetation the bluestems, which mingle on equal terms with short grasses on the lower reaches of the Republican and Smoky Hill, give way to earth-hugging buffalo grass as one travels westward, steadily climbing. Also, corn gives way to wheat as a principal crop, though corn is grown farther west in Nebraska than it is in Kansas. Drought-resistant sorghums, especially developed for this region by state agricultural experiment stations, assume more important roles in the farm economy, and there is somewhat less diversity of crops. Trees become fewer and smaller, the woods on riverbanks consist at last chiefly of stunted cottonwood thickets, and the rivers themselves are generally wide and shallow: they carry less water, of course, as one moves toward their sources. On every hand the horizons widen out, farther and farther, toward the immense solitudes of the High Plains.

These, the High Plains, constitute the _western_ landscape of the basin. On first acquaintance they appear to be a vast flat monotony, a waveless sea of earth circled by a distant rim of sky: the prevailing color is brown, or gold, or faded yellow-green, depending on the season and the rainfall. The plains seem utterly featureless. One is aware at first only of vast empty spaces and feels the terror or the gratefulness of them. But as one comes to know these plains better, he perceives that they are _not_ feature-less. There are austere beauties composed, with classic restraint, of the simplest elements: a towering cloud mass hued with evening in the west, a subtle variation in the pattern of wheat and short milos and buffalo grass, a lonely farmhouse standing strangely proud and somber at the edge of a shallow ravine.

Here trees, by their rarity, become centers of the watcher's attention; instead of merely ornamenting a view, they become the ordering principles of it. For this is all short-grass country of little rain, a magnificent range for buffalo and antelope and elk in those wilderness years when it was mapped as the "Great American Desert," a magnificent range for cattle when the railroads first opened it to Eastern markets. Great stretches of range, fenced now, yet remain—but this is predominantly a land of wheat, and there are few sights more impressive or more lovely than the golden fields just before harvest, flowing in endless waves before the wind. Afterward the fields are plowed and cheerless, helpless against whatever heavy rain may come or against the ceaseless wind if rain comes not at all. The rivers in this country are all shallow and mostly of intermittent flow; their sandy beds often swallow completely the water assigned to them by the surrounding fields. . . .

2

The Watershed as Process   The watershed, however, is not only landscape; it is also a natural process, and there is evident in nature a tendency of all processes to "strike a balance" and of all variations of phenomena to "smooth themselves out."

The water in two jars sitting side by side on a table and connected by a tube will seek the same level, water flowing from the more to the less full until a balance is struck: this is the essential process of a siphon, or of a waterworks operated by gravity. Two salt solutions of different densities, separated by a permeable membrane, will tend to equalize their concentrations, solvent flowing from the less to the more dense until the difference is erased: this is the essential process of osmosis. Bodies of different temperatures lying side by side will tend toward the same temperature, the warmer body losing heat and the cooler one gaining it until equality is achieved: this is the essential process described by the second law of thermodynamics.

This general tendency of nature toward a silent, motionless monotony is well and widely known. It has been used to sustain all manner of pessimistic philosophies. The universe is running down, some say, and all things sink or rise toward the same dead level. The sun is a cooling star, they say, and all vital tensions are being slowly but inexorably relaxed as the energizing differences are, one by one, removed. The process is reflected, some say, in our cultural landscape: here, too, the tendency is toward a dull uniform mediocrity as a "well-adjusted personality" (a "mature mind") becomes the major aim of individuals in a society that pursues "equality."

Such pessimism gains plausibility from the fact that its corrective, in nature and society, is less widely known and far less perfectly understood. Nevertheless, there is a force which raises mountains and thus counteracts the leveling process of land erosion. Mount Everest is now reported to measure 600 feet higher than the 29,002 feet originally assigned to her—and this may not be due to a mistake in the original measurement, according to some geologists, but to the fact that the Himalayas continue rapidly to rise. Similarly do great men arise out of the cultural landscape, men whose creative effort prevents utter social stagnation. In general there seem to be factors which interrupt and revitalize what must otherwise be a dull, physical chain of action-reaction proceeding steadily, predictably, fatally. . . .

In any case, when we look upon our Kansas Basin as a natural process, or a compendium of natural processes, we might expect to find it seeking a balance of forces within it. We'd expect to detect a leveling procedure whereby that which is high is lowered and that which is low is raised; we'd expect water, seeking its own level and operating on erosible materials, to wear away the uplands and build up, with erosion debris, the lowlands; and we'd expect the rivers to flow ever more sluggishly as the process continued, tending toward an ultimate stagnant sea spread thinly over a land surface utterly flat. We'd expect to find vegetable and animal life tending toward stability, seeking and perhaps achieving a balance in which the death of one fed the life of another, and the waste products of one were the vital sustenance of another—while all proceeded together, with seeming inevitability, toward ultimate extinction. The unhappy end would be so far distant, however, as to be imperceptible, and we could expect its prevention, at some future time, by a new creative cataclysm. . . . All this we'd expect to find—and all this we *do* find.

Some 40,000,000 years ago began the mountain-folding revolution, called the Cainozoic, which produced the Rocky Mountains as it did the Andes, the Alps, the Himalayas, and virtually every other lofty peak on the earth today. This was, or is (for it is still going on), the third such revolution during the last 300,000,000 years, and each has had as its cause the shrinkage and crumbling of the earth's crust as it very slowly cools over that intensely hot molten material which still comprises all but a tiny fraction of the earth's total mass. Cooling means contraction, and it has been estimated that the outer 249 miles of the earth's radius has, as it solidified, been reduced by some 15 miles. This has meant a reduction of 93 miles in the earth's circumference and of some 1,545,000 square miles of the earth's total surface. The reduction has not, of course, been uniform: some portions have shrunk more than others, with resulting pimples and wrinkles across the world's face. As George Gamow puts it in his fascinating *Biography of the Earth:*[1] "[We] conclude that not less than 100 million cubic kilometers of solid rock must have been pushed out above the surface of the Earth in the form of various mountain ranges and high plateaux."

It was the latest mountain-folding revolution, heaving up the Rockies, which tilted Kansas from east to west and provided the profile which ever since has been sculptured by wind and water. The resulting Kansas landscape is yet a "young" one. The force which chiefly ages it is erosion by that running water so often used as symbol for Time, and it has not yet brought our land-scape to full "maturity," much less to "old age" or "senility."[2] The High Plains are not yet deeply marked by streams and rivers; erosion has carved there very few well-defined hills and valleys; and in the lower portions of the basin steep lime-ridged valley walls show that even here erosion has much work to do before

[1]New York: Viking Press, 1941. Published as Pelican Mentor Book by the New American Library of Literature, Inc., in 1948.

[2]For those of us who try to learn how to think about a river there is significance in the fact that geologists, speaking of landscape as process, employ *vital* metaphors, as though the analogy between our Kansas Basin and a living body were not only poetic but also useful—and useful because it is in some sense "true."

our landscape assumes the "low uniform relief" characteristic of late maturity. Nevertheless, a considerable aging *has* occurred: though the body of our land remains youthful it is certainly not "infantile." And when the white man came he found on the surface of this land such ecological balance as can be achieved only through long ages of vital struggle.

This balance of life forces—a very delicate one—inhibited the leveling tendency of water and wind erosion across the watershed. Woods covered hillsides in the eastern portion of the basin, and the leaf mulch which formed beneath them soaked up rain like a blotter. The bluestem grasses of the Flint Hills section—rising tall as a man on horseback where conditions were most favorable —shattered heavy summer and autumn rains into a fine dew gently falling upon the earth and easily absorbable by it. Farther west the carpet of curling buffalo grass performed a similar function. A thick dead residue of earlier generations of plant life, and a tangle of living roots, tied down the soil and enriched it. Animals and insects were all involved, with these plants, in a precise system of checks and balances.

Indians had done virtually nothing to disturb this system. For one thing, they were few in number: it's doubtful if as many as 7,000 ever lived at one time in the 60,060 square miles of the basin. For another, their methods of cultivating maize and beans and squash, when they cultivated at all, were not conducive to greatly accelerated soil erosion. The Kansas or Kaw Indians may be taken as typical of the settled as distinct from the nomadic tribes in the area. They numbered but 1,606 in 1835, and presumably this was approximately their number before 1830, when their village of semi-permanent earth lodges stood at the mouth of the Blue, where Manhattan now stands. (By 1872, in consequence of the white man's gifts of liquor and smallpox, the population was reduced to approximately 200.) The Kaw braves hunted buffalo and other game, and warred with their hereditary foes, the Pawnees, whose lands were to the south; the Kaw squaws worked the tiny fields with tools too crude to disturb greatly the soil's natural cover; and all of them were, typically, creatures rather than contradictions of the basin as natural landscape and process.

Vivid word pictures of the country as it was in its virgin state are contained in the beautifully written reports which Brevet Captain John C. Frémont[3] made of the exploring expeditions he led to the Rocky Mountains in 1842 and to Oregon and North California in 1843 and '44. He found that land sweet which was later to be so maligned by tourists and even by its own inhabitants. "Everywhere the rose is met with," he wrote in June of 1842 as he moved up the valley of the Kaw, "and reminds us of cultivated gardens and civilization. It is scattered over the prairies in small bouquets, and, when glittering in the dews and waving in the pleasant breeze of the early morning, is the most beautiful of the prairie flowers." He wrote lyrically of the beauties of the hills later called Flint. In June of 1843 he again traveled westward along the Kaw, arriving on the eighth at the junction of the Smoky Hill and Republican rivers, where the town of Junction City now stands. Proceeding up the Republican: "Now and then we caught a glimpse of a small herd of elk; and occasionally a band of antelopes, whose curiosity sometimes brought them within rifle range, would circle round us, and then scour off into the prairies. . . . The country was everywhere covered with a considerable variety of grasses—occasionally poor and thin, but far more frequently luxuriant and rich. . . . At noon on [June] 23rd, we descended into the valley of a principal fork of the Republican, a beautiful stream with a dense border of wood, consisting principally of varieties of ash, forty feet wide and four feet deep. It was musical with the notes of many birds, which, from the vast expanse of

[3]This was the Frémont who became a national figure as a result of his Western explorations and in 1856 was nominated as candidate for President by the newly formed Republican party.

silent prairie around, seemed all to have collected here. We continued during the afternoon our route along the river, which was populous with prairie dogs (the bottoms being entirely occupied with their villages), and late in the evening encamped on its banks. The prevailing timber is a blue-foliaged ash, and ash-leaved maple. With these were . . . cottonwood, and long-leaved willow." As he proceeded, the character of the country abruptly changed: he left the Kansas Basin and entered that of the Platte, but the High Plains onto which he moved were continuous with those we've described as the *western* landscape of our watershed, and though he speaks here of "parched" and "sterile" country, and of a "desert" landscape, it is significant that he also speaks of immense herds of buffalo and an abundance of other grazing wildlife. . . .

It was a lovely unspoiled land seen by this remarkably sensitive and intelligent young man. One is mistaken who assumes, however, as some conservation enthusiasts have done, that stream pollution and floods and an ugly soil erosion were wholly absent from it. These are not (as we've said) unnatural phenomena produced entirely by the white man's enterprise: rather are they integral to the watershed as natural process. There were occasional pollutions of streams by the dung and dead carcasses of animals. There was some natural pollution by salt brines in central Kansas. There were areas of naked soil gouged by gullies, swept by clouds of dust, and worn away by sheet erosion. There were certainly mighty floods down the rivers—floods whose crests were as high as any recorded in the white man's history, and perhaps higher.

The very first glimpse which history gives us of the Missouri River shows it in flood, thick with mud and clogged with debris. Francis Parkman in his *La Salle and the Discovery of the Great West* tells how Marquette and Joliet paddled their birch-bark canoes down the Mississippi in June of 1673, and how they saw,

some miles below the mouth of the Illinois and to their left, a
huge rock cliff on which were painted a pair of monsters, all red
and black and green. These manitous or Indian gods frightened
Marquette, as he frankly states in his journal. He and his com-
panions talked of them for a long time as they continued downstream.

"They were thus engaged," writes Parkman, "when they were
suddenly aroused by a real danger. A torrent of yellow mud
rushed furiously athwart the calm blue current of the Mississippi;
boiling and surging, and sweeping in its course logs, branches,
and uprooted trees. They had reached the mouth of the Missouri,
where that savage river, descending from its mad career through
a vast unknown of barbarism, poured its turbid floods into the
bosom of its gentler sister. Their light canoes whirled on the miry
vortex like dry leaves on an angry brook. 'I never,' writes Marquette, 'saw anything more terrific. . . .'"

Father Membre's account of La Salle's expedition in 1681 and
1682 confirms this first impression of the Missouri as a turbid
river, dark yellow with eroded soil. He writes:

"Then [on January 13, 1682] we set out [from the mouth of the
Illinois], and, six leagues lower down, found the Ozage [Mis-
souri] river coming from the west. It is full as large as the river
Colbert [Mississippi], into which it empties, troubling it so much
that from the mouth of the Ozage the water is hardly drinkable.
. . . [It] pours in so much mud that, from its mouth, the water
of the great river, whose bed is also slimy, is more like clear mud
than river water."

Be it remembered that one element of the "vast unknown of
barbarism" from which the Missouri descended in its "mad
career" was the Kansas River Basin. And some of the "clear mud"
which Father Membre describes was poured into the Missouri
through the mouth of the Kaw. Frémont himself, whose first expedition went up the Kaw twelve years before the white man

began his settlements there, tells in his report of reaching a ford in the late afternoon of June 14, 1842, only to find that "it [the river] had been swollen by the late rains, and was sweeping by with an angry current, yellow and turbid as the Missouri." Two years later, in 1844, occurred the highest flood ever recorded on the lower Missouri, when a high crest coming down the Kaw coincided with one coming down the upper reaches of the Big Muddy.

But though stream pollution and floods and soil erosion are thus shown to have occurred under "natural" conditions, there can be small doubt that the white man's enterprise and carelessness have increased the former two while accelerating the latter. This is attested to by the accounts of other early travelers and by many portions of Frémont's own report. These contain references to "crystal-clear" streams abounding in fish, streams that now are thick with mud and afford small sport to fishermen. Frémont writes of making bivouac on "some well-timbered ravines near the Little Blue" and of "crossing the next morning a number of handsome streams with clear water and sandy beds." One would not find those streams so handsome today, nor be able to see, through their veils of dark water, whether their beds were rock or sand or black oozy earth. The very name of the Blue indicates a great change in its appearance during the last century, a change which measures a vast increase in its pollution. According to some sources, the river was so named because, when first seen by white men, it *was* blue; it reflected like crystal the azure heavens. Now its prevailing color is a dirty yellow-brown.

Moreover, the early history of the Kansas-Nebraska territory reveals main rivers to have been navigable far above their mouths, rivers that now are strewn with shoals of sand and too shallow, when not in flood or near it, to bear craft drawing much deeper than a rowboat. Edward Everett Hale, in his remarkably accurate *Kanzas and Nebraska* (a book published in 1854 to help the work of the Emigrant Aid Company), writes of the "Kanzas river" as navigable from its mouth all the way to the Republican Fork, save in seasons of drought. The Republican, too, "is navigable farther up" beyond its lowest reaches, though "no explorations have been made public to show how far." He points out that "a steamboat carried up the supplies needed for the building of Fort Riley, the new government post at the mouth of the Republican Fork."

3

The Watershed in History   It has often been remarked that man, as he feeds and clothes and shelters himself, as he multiplies and increasingly exploits nature in support of his civilization, has long been a major geologic force in the world. Even this assessment of his material powers seems too modest in this twentieth century. In our own time man may become a force whose magnitude is comparable with that by which the earth was made, for it now appears that he (who so often remains a savage at heart) will have in his hands all too soon the power to dissolve into dust the whole body of our planet. When one says this one is saying that ideas and attitudes, passions and criteria of value, are geologic forces, for it is through these that men are moved to define their characters in terms of their environment. Useful in our attempt to learn how to think about a river is a realization of this mysterious continuity of flesh and idea, spirit and body, whereby one manifests the other and is determined by it. The essential mind-body process cannot even be termed an *inter*action, it appears, for there seems ultimately to be no gap by which the one is divided into two. . . .

There's a true sense, then, in which men's ideals of justice and human rights have operated as geologic forces upon the Kansas Basin—for it was the issue between those who abhorred Negro slavery and those who sought to extend it that first brought the white man in multitudes to the eastern portion of this region. These first settlers set the tone for the Kansas community; had their values been different, their effects upon the basin as landscape and process would have been subtly different.

The first large wave of migration to Kansas was determined by Stephen Douglas's effort, in 1854, to compromise the issue between North and South in such a way as to secure the presidency for himself. His effort was the Kansas-Nebraska Bill, which repealed the Missouri Compromise and, through its principle of "squatter sovereignty," virtually invited North and South to fight it out for possession of the territory. Abolitionists and pro-slavery advocates at once organized societies to promote emigration to Kansas, both groups coming armed for battle, and Bleeding Kansas with her murderous John Brown and Charles Hamelton, her flamboyant Jim Lane and Jim Montgomery, her raids and counterraids by "Jayhawkers" and "Border Ruffians," provided dress rehearsal during the following years for national Civil War. By the time that war came, Kansas was definitely "free" soil. The census of 1860 showed a population of 107,206 people, of whom nearly three fourths were anti-slavery, and when Kansas was admitted to the Union on January 29, 1861, the New England puritanism which had animated many of the Abolitionist leaders was a dominant characteristic of the new state's mental climate.

This religious idealism was sustained by the colonies of Swedish Lutherans, German Mennonites;[1] and Pennsylvania Dutch River Brethren who, among other religious groups, came to Kansas in the '70s. They settled for the most part just west of the bluestem region, in that _middle_ landscape where tall and short grass met and mingled—and there they encountered a very different way of life embodied in the Indian fighters, the buffalo hunters, the cowboys, and the kind of gambling farmer who moved out

[1]They came by way of the Ukraine, bringing with them the hard red winter wheat on which the state's wheat economy was based.

into the inhospitable High Plains. Abilene, for example, gained world-wide fame (or notoriety) in the late 1860s as the wildest cow town in the Wild West, the end of the Chisholm Trail up which Texas cattle were driven by the hundred thousand for shipment East on the Kansas Pacific—and it was to Abilene that the pious, pacifistic River Brethren came in 1872, including the Eisenhower family, whose descendants were to give Abilene its second burst of world fame in the 1940s. West of Abilene developed the economy of wheat and cattle and oil, risky for the individual though fabulously lucrative on the whole and over the long run, involving men whose gambling and fighting values were much more closely akin to those of the Southern Cavalier than to those of the New England Puritan.

In the Nebraska and Kansas portions of the basin, historical and cultural developments were sufficiently similar to those along the same longitudes in Kansas to justify a use of the latter to typify the whole.

Out of this complex of factors emerged a curious regional psychology, one which mingled a pious idealism with the most ruthless pragmatism and sought consciously to perpetuate an agricultural society against industrializing and urbanizing forces As Charles C. Howes writes in his *This Place Called Kansas*,[2] "Farming was looked upon [by the state's leaders] as the most guileless of endeavors, and farm people were regarded as inherently chaste because of their nearness to the soil." There was displayed often an actual eagerness to legislate private morality (there was "bone-dry" liquor prohibition in Kansas until 1948, cigarette sales were prohibited in the state in the 1920s, and the college town of Manhattan did not permit Sunday picture shows until the mid-1930s) by people who bitterly opposed regulation of private economic enterprise and any such positive governmental enterprise as might effect a valley-wide development plan.

[2]Norman: University of Oklahoma Press, 1952.

All this produced an effect on the basin as landscape and process somewhat different from what would otherwise have been produced. Industrialization of the region (such as began to occur in the 1940s) would have meant a different quality if not a larger quantity of stream pollution. This pollution would almost certainly have been more dangerous had not Kansans, in their Puritan conviction that "cleanliness is next to godliness," enacted effective public health legislation in the early decades of this century. (They were among the first in America to do so.) On the other hand, soil conservation, flood control, and irrigation might have been farther advanced had the people been more committed to the values of co-operation and less to "rugged individualism," and had they not remained (in my opinion) so blindly distrustful of all positive governmental enterprise. Impossible to assess in "geologic" terms is the resistance of the region's leaders to huge "corporate farming" such as John Bird attempted in western Kansas two decades ago,[3] but there's at least the possibility that there'd have been much more wind erosion across the High Plains in the '30s and '40s had Bird's experiment succeeded. There's the contrary possibility that such wind erosion would have been reduced, since corporation management might have "put each acre to its proper use" to a degree often not possible on small, family-sized farms.

All these historical peculiarities of the watershed, however, can have produced but minor variations in the general pattern of the American's exploitation, a pattern applicable to a hundred large watersheds. To this virgin Kansas Basin, as to a hundred similar

[3]The general Kansas reaction to Bird's effort to transform farming into a large-scale industry was violently negative. Many thought this effort to destroy the family-owned and -operated farm smacked of immorality, and popular pressure forced the legislature to outlaw such huge enterprises. Whether such legislation, by itself, would have been effective is doubtful, but the Depression put an end to Bird's company. It went bankrupt, having overexpanded.

valleys, the white man came with his plow and his ax and his vast destructive carelessness. He took much from the earth, and from the waters flowing across and under the earth—and he gave little back in a life-nourishing form. He plowed up grasslands, cut down woods, and started living on the fat capital of the soil instead of the interest, as other life had done. He built towns along the streams, and instead of returning his organic wastes to the soil as other animals had done he flushed them into rivers which were often, by reason of their increased silt load, ill equipped to digest them. He drained water from the rivers, and from the ground through wells, for irrigation and domestic and industrial purposes, and then increased the menace to his own health while reducing his own recreational facilities by pouring into these same waters his industrial wastes. The inevitable consequence was a complex of problems in water and soil economy, increasingly serious and increasingly difficult to solve.

There is clear evidence, for example, that the incidence and severity of floods have been vastly increased. Consider the main stem of the Blue. The country along it was settled in the 1850s, but not until 1886 was a flood recorded there. The next flood down the Blue occurred in 1902—and since then floods have occurred on an average of once every two and a half years. In 1950 and '51 the flooding was exceptionally severe.

Of Sewage and Civilization

1

To Begin with— Considered in functional terms, the river is many things. Potentially or actually or historically, it is an artery of commerce. It is a stream of raw power, capable of being refined into wired electricity. It is a menace to be guarded against, lest it overwhelm the works of man. It is an opportunity to transform parched lands into gardens. It is a source of drinking water. It is also a sewer.

Each of these functions presents the river to our mind as a problem. It is a problem of creating or maintaining a navigable channel, a problem of hydroelectric-power development, a problem of flood control, a problem of irrigation, a problem of safe municipal water supply. It is also a problem of pollution abatement.

We may focus on any of these as we try to learn how to think about a river—but of them all, at the outset, the river as sewer and as pollution problem must seem to most of us the least interesting, the most repulsive. Factors in this problem are the offal of packing plants, the dung of man and beast, the wastes of manufacturing, the brine of oil fields, the debris of soil erosion. How could a subject made up of such elements fail to be boring as well as unpleasant?

No doubt you are willing to grant at the outset that the subject is an important one. It's important to you and me personally, touching us in many and various ways.

If you'd like to use your neighborhood waters for fishing and swimming or boating, water pollution has a good deal to do with your recreation. If you love the look of clean sweet streams and lakes in a green landscape, it has something to do with the aesthetic values of your life. It has some influence on your personal income, in so far as this is bound up with the economic and social welfare of your region. It may quite directly affect your occupation if you are a farmer or are employed in an industry which uses large quantities of water in its processes. Most important of all, of course, it has to do with the health and well-being of you and your community. Unpleasant though the thought of it may be, the water you use in your household today is likely to be water that has been fouled and purified and then fouled again and purified again, over and over, before it reaches you: to be even more blunt about it, the water which goes down your gullet today may have gone last week through someone else's kidneys and intestines: and if it happens to reach you without adequate cleaning up, you're in trouble. Serious trouble.

Nevertheless, "pollution" is a particularly unlovely word, and you may fail to see how its connection with our inland waters can be expected to define a subject of general interest, however fascinating it may be to sanitary engineers, public health officers, doctors of medicine, and the like. I think you'll change your mind, however, if you'll "dig into" this seemingly nauseous concern. You'll discover that boredom in this case, as in so many others, is but an aspect of ignorance. As knowledge increases, boredom flees. The subject assumes ever-deeper significances. The area of its implication widens to include matters interesting to all of us, and what seems at first fit for only the most pedestrian prose may come to seem a proper subject for flights of lyricism, if one chooses to make them.

You may recall that Victor Hugo did so choose when, in *Les Miserables*, he wrote his famous treatise on the sewers of Paris. He called it "The Interior of Leviathan," and in it he suggested that much of civilization's political economy, its system of values, its tendency toward death and dissolution, can be measured by the manner in which it handles its sewage. The Parisian manner, he cried, is a disastrous error. The refuse of the city which should manure the plain is, instead, "swept into the gulf." He went on, in typically exuberant hyperbole:

"Do you know what these piles or ordure are, collected at the corners of streets, those carts of mud carried off at night from the streets, the frightful barrels of the night-man, the fetid streams of subterranean mud which the pavement conceals from you? All this is a flowering field; it is green grass, it is mint and thyme and sage, it is game, it is cattle, it is the satisfied lowing of heavy kine at night, it is perfumed hay, it is golden wheat, it is bread on your table, it is warm blood in your veins, it is health, it is joy, it is life."

A sewer, he proclaims, is a mistake.

" 'The drains of Rome,' says Liebig, 'absorbed the entire welfare of the Roman Peasant.' When the Campagna of Rome was ruined by the Roman drains, Rome exhausted Italy, and when it had placed Italy in its cloaca, it poured into it Sicily, and then Sardinia, and then Africa. The drains of Rome swallowed up the world. . . ." As for Paris: "Each eructation of our drains costs us one thousand francs, and this has two results—the earth impoverished and the water poisoned; hunger issuing from the furrow and sickness from the river. It is notorious that at this very hour the Thames poisons London! and [in Paris] it has been found necessary to remove most of the mouths of the sewers down the river below the last bridge."

2

Four Glimpses from History   Victor Hugo's interest in sewage disposal, his sense of its importance to history, has not, alas, been shared by many historians. An unfortunate fastidiousness, joined perhaps by lack of industry and a failure of imagination, seems to have operated as censor, denying to written history all but the meagerest references to the matters which here concern us.

Indeed, you may have noticed and deplored a general tendency of historians to ignore much of truly *vital* import in history, while giving vastly disproportionate accounts of Big Shots and of the Great Events in which Big Shots play their self-important roles. The froth is mistaken for the wave of history. What of soil depletion and erosion as factors in the decline and fall of the Roman Empire? Gibbon, in his monumental work, scarcely mentions it. What of malaria as a weakener of Italian vitality in the centuries following Augustus? Again there is almost complete silence. Who knows the names of Rome's greatest architects, her hydraulic engineers, her civil engineers, men whose discoveries permanently enriched our skills and whose constructions still stand throughout the Mediterranean world as evidence of their genius?

We hear of Sextus Julius Frontinus, the engineer who headed Rome's water department in A.D. 100. We hear of him but faintly, and only because he himself wrote books still extant. We hear of others not at all.

Thus my own sketchy research into the ancient and medieval history of sewage disposal has not given me as much information as I'd like. It has, however, indicated that the problem began when men first crowded into cities and that the manner of its solution can tell us a great deal about the standards of living and the rights of ordinary people in earlier civilizations.

The relative importance of property rights and individual human values can be so measured. It may be stated as maxim that sanitary sewage disposal varies in direct proportion, *not* to technical competence (which is sometimes much higher than prevailing sewage-disposal methods would indicate), but to the social importance of ordinary citizens. Only as ordinary men become influential, either by direct participation in policy making or by mass pressures on policy makers—only then do we find large-scale water and sewer developments. Rigidly stratified societies are virtually certain to avoid such expenditures unless and until the ruling elite recognizes that its own physical health, its creature comforts, and its social privileges are threatened by lack of them.

In medieval England, for instance, sanitary policy seems not to have begun until a king was personally offended by the filthy habits of his subjects. In a royal order to the mayor and sheriffs of London, issued in 1357, Edward III tells how, as he rode along the Thames, he "beheld dung and lay-stalls and other filth accumulated in divers places in the said City upon the bank of the said river" and "also perceived the fumes and other abominable stenches arising therefrom: from the corruption of which, if tolerated, great peril, as well to the persons dwelling within the said City as to the nobles and others passing along the river, will

it is feared arise unless indeed some fitting remedy be speedily
provided for the same." The city government thereupon pre-
scribed that "for saving the body of the river, and preserving the
quays . . . for lading and unlading, as also for avoiding the
filthiness that is increasing in the river and upon the banks of the
Thames, to the great abomination and damage of the people,"
rubbish and filth were not henceforth to be thrown into the
Thames or "Flete" but must be taken out of the city by carts. But
Simon, in his authoritative book, *English Sanitary Institutions*,
indicates that Edward's will was by no means fully executed, for
in 1372 another royal order complains "that 'rushes, dung, refuse,
and other filth and harmful things . . . from City and suburbs
are thrown into the water of Thames, so that the water afore-
said and the hythes thereof are so greatly obstructed, and the
course of the said water so greatly narrowed, that great ships are
not able, as of old they were wont, any longer to come up to the
said City, but are impeded therein: and the writ enjoins immediate measures to amend this state of things, and to prevent recur-
rence.'"

Medieval England was of course a crudely primitive land when
measured against earlier civilizations. Undoubtedly the Lon-
dinium of the Romans, with 60,000 souls and paved and sewered
streets, was much more sanitary than the London of Edward III.
But in many of these earlier civilizations, sanitary engineering,
though technically quite highly developed, seems to have been
confined for the most part to the palaces of kings, priests, and
noblemen.

On the island of Crete, for example, there had developed by
2000 B.C. a civilization not only rich in artistic talent but skillful
in the sanitary disposal of its rubbish—a combination of talent
and skill which is by no means inevitable. (The greatest artists
often know little of plumbing, and there are people of doubtful
wisdom who talk as though America's skill in the latter were

actually hostile to art.) The largest city of Crete was Knossos. It is famed in Greek mythology as the capital of King Minos, whose palace, the Labyrinth, was guarded by the frightful Minotaur. Actually all Cretan rulers seem to have been called Minos, just as all Egyptian rulers were called Pharaoh, and archaeologists have found the Labyrinth to be "a building as stately, complex, and luxurious as any in the ancient world." The quotation is from H. G. Wells, who goes on to say that we find here "waterpipes, bathrooms, and the like conveniences, such as have hitherto been regarded as the latest refinements of modern life." We find, too, a notable sanitation system. Huge circular stone-walled pits, called kouloura and arranged in line, were constructed for the sanitary disposal of rubbish. Earth was apparently used in layers to prevent noxious odors, and surface water was drained into them to aid the digestion of sewage. This skill, however, was confined to the palace area. There seems to be no evidence that it was widely applied to the welfare of the masses.

In the Indus Valley of northwest India, on the other hand, the evidence is clear. This remarkable civilization, whose remains have been but lately discovered, flourished in 3000 B.C., and it was even then millennia old, for it was of vast extent and advanced organization. Unlike the early civilizations of Mesopotamia and Egypt, that of the Indus Valley was predominantly secular: religion, though present, did not have ruling power: and there is perhaps a causal connection between this fact and the fact that Mohenjo-Daro, the chief city thus far excavated, had splendid sewers. Priest-ridden societies are despotic in form and otherworldly in outlook. Their engineering talents are (as we've indicated) generally devoted to the dwellings of rulers, the monuments by which rulers glorify themselves, and the temples whose worship is a pacifier of miserable men. But at Mohenjo-Daro the most elaborate structures were designed for the use of citizens (one public bath covered a large block), and the water and sewer systems compared not unfavorably with those of American cities today. Many of the houses were of two stories and had bathrooms. Their drains were connected into covered sewers which ran along the streets, feeding into trunk lines which, in turn, fed into the river. Every street, every alleyway, every passage had its own covered conduits of finely shaped and precisely laid brick.

As for ancient Rome, she began her career as a republic, and her later empire had a wider diffusion of governing power and a closer concern for the popular will than any preceding great state had had. It seems fitting, therefore, that among the first of her massive engineering enterprises was the Cloaca Maxima.

The stone arches of this mighty sewer were so wide and tall that a wagon loaded with hay could pass under them. Into it fed a large and increasingly complex sewer system draining off not only the city's refuse and storm water but also the marshes which divided the Seven Hills and upon whose dried beds, as the city grew, were raised tenements and palaces and great public buildings. The Cloaca Maxima opened into the Tiber, which also served as a main source of city water until Appius Claudius the Blind built the first aqueduct in 312 B.C. Subsequently thirteen other aqueducts were built, the average length being slightly less than 100 miles, and they carried 300,000,000 gallons of fresh water daily from the mountains to giant city reservoirs. From these latter was piped water for household use, for magnificent public baths, for tremendous mock sea battles in the arenas—and for sewage disposal.

The Roman cities were perhaps more sanitary, in general, than any of their predecessors had been. Certainly their engineering devices for insuring a clean fresh-water supply and for flushing out their waste products were considerably in advance of those in earlier great towns—with the possible exception of the ancient Indus cities about which so little is known. As masters of hydraulics the Romans were tremendous. But they neglected certain other matters of vital concern, and one portent of their ultimate doom was the darkly flowing Tiber, thick with eroded soil from the uplands. The river's pollution plagued Rome, and literally, through all the long ages of her greatness. It was partly in consequence that there developed, in the late years of the empire, the beginnings at least of a system of public health officers: Gibbon tells how Valentinian, about A.D. 370, established "fourteen skillful physicians, with stipends and privileges, in the fourteen quarters of Rome."

For Rome, at the height of her glory, remained by modern American standards sick and filthy—and sick *because* filthy. She was so sick in an average year that a modern American would have hesitated to visit her. Typhoid fever and dysentery were in continuous epidemic, tuberculosis carried off whole families, malaria enervated the body politic through three centuries before the German barbarians destroyed it completely; and all these are diseases whose transmission is associated with polluted waters.[1]

Nor is it irrelevant to point out that Rome inherited from the preceding great powers in her theater of operations a "disease" of soil impoverishment and erosion which, under Roman organization, became progressively more serious. Such a disease accelerates as it proceeds. In the later years of the empire it became a kind of "galloping consumption" which transformed fertile plains into sandy deserts, shredded fat slopes into raw gullies, and ripped the soil off denuded mountains at the greatest rate, perhaps, that it ever achieved until we Americans set out to ruin a continent. Victor Hugo should have meant soil erosion as well as

[1]This is not to say that tuberculosis and malaria are *chiefly* transmitted by polluted waters, but that the former *may* spread from the ill to the well through unsanitary drinking water, while malarial mosquitoes breed best in stagnant, fetid waters which result when lakes and streams are clogged with debris.

soil exhaustion when he spoke of Italy, and Sicily, and Sardinia, and North Africa as pouring down the insatiable Roman gullet. And to the lands he mentioned should have been added Spain, Greece, Palestine, Phoenicia, the whole of the Middle East.

I myself have seen the vast yellow deserts of Syria, where rich soil once nourished immense populations. It was counted the most stable and prosperous of Roman provinces; twelve millions lived in plenty where three now live in poverty. I've walked the streets of Palmyra, once the rich and powerful center of a flourishing culture and now an immense, solitary ruin in a waste of naked pebbles. I've stood above Tyre and Sidon on the Lebanon where great cedars grew for Solomon's temple and for the palaces of Pharaohs—bare now, and reduced to subsoil and naked rock. Erosion by wind and water wrought these sad changes. And such bitter sights must convince the most skeptical that man's violation of nature's economy is a grievous sin whose wages are, indeed, death. And desolation.

Now the relevance of soil exhaustion to public health in the ancient Mediterranean world did not consist alone of its effects on food supply, which was of course reduced in quantity and nutritional value. It consisted also of the effects upon streams and rivers which, clogged with erosion debris, became so turbid that they could no longer cleanse themselves in a few flowing miles of the organic wastes dumped into them. The Tiber, which could easily have digested the sewage of early Rome, may well have become a stinking, disease-breeding mass of liquid mud below Rome in the later days of the empire (we know that the river had to be repeatedly dredged in order to maintain its channel)—and similar catastrophes must have befallen other streams flowing past mighty cities. Moreover, downstream lakes and reservoirs, filling with silt, must often have been transformed into swampy breeding grounds for malarial mosquitoes. This may partially account for the fact that malaria, which turns virile men into listless weaklings in ever-recurring spasms, was apparently not widespread in Italy until some years after the birth of Christ. . . .

3

Suggestions from History   Let us now sum up our four sketches from history and see what lessons are in them for us. They've been presented, as you've observed, in a certain order: an order of the increasing social importance of ordinary citizens as this is measured by sewage-disposal systems. You may also have observed that this order coincides with another: in each of our examples the sewage and pollution problem has a wider area of reference than it had in its predecessor.

In medieval London the problem presented itself as an annoyance and possible health threat to the nobility, and the attempt to solve it, focused exclusively on the Thames, consisted simply of ordering common folk to relocate their latrines, to cease dumping into the river, and to cart their refuse instead from the city.

In ancient Crete we found a much greater technical skill displayed in the construction of water and sanitation systems, with effective septic tanks to digest refuse from the palace area. There was no clear evidence, however, that this skill served great masses of people.

In the Indus civilization, on the other hand, ordinary citizens were served by large, complex water and sewer systems, with covered conduits draining houses, feeding into lines along the streets, and thence into trunk lines opening upon the river.

And in Rome also this is true. But our more extensive knowledge of Rome enables us to see her sewage and pollution problem as part of a much larger problem of water economy. The use of rivers for sewage disposal was complicated by erosion of the uplands, which also had unhappy effects upon navigation, water supply, and, undoubtedly, the use of inland waters for recreation.

Clearly, it is from the Roman experience that we Americans have most to learn. It teaches us that stream pollution, and the use of streams for sewage disposal, is by no means a problem of the stream alone, nor is it exclusively a problem of the stream and its immediately contiguous land. It is also a problem of the uplands and their uses. The stream is but part of a landscape. It is an organic element of a watershed whose various problems are all interrelated, being but aspects of one total problem, and this means that the stream cannot on a large scale or in the long run be treated successfully as an isolated thing. At the beginning of large-scale plans, the whole watershed must be considered as organism. Otherwise the plans may fail in the end.

The Romans themselves never really learned this lesson. They resembled us Americans in that they were the great administrators, organizers, and engineers of their age—and the greatest exploiters of natural resources. They also resembled us, and differed greatly from the Greeks, in that they were, by and large, a remarkably unphilosophic race. Slowly, partially, and too late, the more astute among them came to realize that some of the roots of their urban civilization were withering for lack of natural sustenance. We find Cyprian, in the third century A.D., bemoaning the fact that "the world has grown old and does not remain in its former vigor"; that "the rainfall . . . is diminishing" and "the metals are nearly exhausted"; and that "the husbandman is failing in the fields." We find increasingly numerous references, in the years of decline, to deforestation, soil exhaustion, and clogged irrigation ditches in deserts which once richly bloomed. But we do not find this consciousness organized into the practical forms needed for a reversal of the anti-vital trend.

The clue to what the Romans should have done, as well as to their failure to do it, may perhaps be found in a famous statement by Cicero. This greatest lawyer of a race of master lawyers was himself a countryman, born and reared in a villa in the foothills of the Apennines, and he was convinced of the necessity for agreement between men's legislation and the natural order of the universe. But, as a Stoic philosopher, he went farther than this; he identified the natural order with man's moral code, assuming the latter, in so far as it was valid, to be the product of an inborn "natural reason." He summed up his basic view as follows:

"True law is right reason in agreement with nature, world-wide in scope, unchanging, everlasting. . . . We may not oppose or alter that law, we cannot abolish it, we cannot be freed from its obligations by any legislature, and we need not look outside ourselves for an expounder of it. This law does not differ for Rome and for Athens, for the present and for the future; . . . it is and it will be valid for all nations and all times. . . . He who disobeys it denies himself and his own nature."

This has the merit of recognizing that there are laws of nature whose contravention by man's legislation always leads, through more or less disaster, to defeat of the latter. We may well applaud the assertion that "right reason in agreement with nature" lies at the root of all just man-made law, and we may regret the Roman failure to apply to problems of land and water use this principle of harmony. But we can also understand the failure when we note that, in Cicero's view, the "law of nature" may be discovered simply by introspection, and that he seems to posit an inflexibility of legal structure which is distinctly *un*natural in that it ignores all elements which are fluid and changing, including the creative elements of human nature. The discovery of nature's laws requires more intellectual humility than Cicero seems to have realized. It requires that we look outside ourselves and subordinate to objective sense-data not only our egoistic wills but also those "self-evident truths" which have so often led philosophers astray. . . .

But we ourselves must not stray into bypaths, however attractive. Suffice it here to remind ourselves that, as we viewed in historic perspective our own use of water and soil in the Kansas

River Basin, we saw little evidence of that "just law" which is "right reason in agreement with nature." Instead we saw repeated again and again the error of assuming that nature will suspend her laws for our convenience, or passively submit to legislation by men who have failed to consult her requirements. Slowly, painfully, and imperfectly, the recognition has been forced upon us that we ourselves are elements in a natural watershed, involved in a natural process, and that we can prosper through the long run only by adapting our practice to nature's precept.

4

From Rome to the Kaw: Two Sources of Water Law   This lesson is nowhere more clearly demonstrated than in our experience with man-made laws governing water use. Here we find, in the vast structure of Roman law, a solid connecting link between the mightiest of ancient empires and our particular problem of stream pollution in the Kansas Basin. If only we had regarded our region in the light of Roman experience when first we came here! We might then have avoided those legal ambiguities and outright contradictions which enabled generations of lawyers, all across the Great Plains, to prosper out of litigation concerning water rights—while the rest of us fussed, and fumed, and paid the costs. . . .

The imperial Romans, lawgivers to all afterages in the Western world, themselves derived much of their law from the Egyptians, the Medes, and the Persians. This seems particularly to have been true of their water laws. All of these earlier peoples, be it noted, inhabited countries where water, by its scarcity, was a precious commodity. None could depend upon rainfall for the growth of crops. All land between the Tigris and Euphrates was intersected by irrigation canals from the earliest dates of recorded history; Egypt depended then as now upon annual inundations by the

Nile; and all the lower plains of Iran were desert where irrigation was not practiced. Inevitably this scarcity of water and the necessity for precisely defined rights in the use of it were reflected in the body of law which slowly developed and which the Romans adopted, added to, and clarified.

The history of Herodotus reveals that as far back as 2300 B.C. governments of subhumid lands faced complicated problems of water use and solved them in ways which led toward later Roman doctrine. A king of Persia, writes Herodotus, had built a dam without sufficiently consulting the needs of farmers downstream. The farmers "who before were in the habit of using the water, not being able to use it any longer, were reduced to great extremities." At last they took their wives and, "standing before the king's palace, raised a great outcry," to which the king responded by ordering that "the gates be opened toward those lands that were most in need; and when their land was satiated by imbibing water, these gates were shut, and others were opened toward those next in greatest need." This solution faced realistically the fact that consumptive use of a limited water supply by one person inevitably reduces its use by others; it also, by calling for best use through the satisfaction of "greatest need," defined an equitable goal toward which those who shape water policy are still struggling in the American West. The difficulty lies, of course, in the definition of "greatest need." It was a difficulty so great that the Romans, a hardheaded race, substituted temporal priority for need in their basic determinations of water rights.

Thus developed the Roman doctrine of prior appropriation, expressed in the oft-quoted maxim of *"qui pior est in tempore, potior est in jure."* We translate it freely as "First in time, first in right." Roman civil law ordained that "ancient water rights, established by long ownership, shall continue to the individual citizens, undisturbed by innovation," and that if a flow of water through certain places "is according to custom and shows usefulness in irrigating certain tracts of land, no innovation against the old form and established custom will be permitted."

But this right by temporal priority was not unqualified in Roman law, which also embodied some elements of "best use" or the satisfaction of "greatest need" in the determination of water property. The law proclaimed that "it is not the acreage, but the use to which water is put, that measures the right to the water." In other words, priorities in time were modified by priorities of uses in the Roman definition of rights. The law ordained that water for domestic use had the prior right, that water for livestock and private gardens was next, that water for fields came third, and that water for mining and mechanical purposes came last. Thus if two men had the same right in time to a severely limited water supply, he who would use it for domestic purposes was given preference over he who would use it to water livestock; he who would water livestock had preference over he who would irrigate fields, and so on.

The Roman laws survived, piecemeal, the collapse of the Roman Empire. They were preserved in partial operation by the Arabs while western Europe went through the Dark Ages, and they provided the bases for legal codes of new European nations when these assertive sovereign powers rose up, bloody-handed, out of the creative chaos of the Renaissance. Having been developed by and for subhumid lands, the Roman water laws in particular survived in Spain, and they were translated into New World terms by the Spanish conquistadors whose seventeenth-century conquests included what is now California, Arizona, New Mexico, Nevada, Utah, Texas.

These Spanish-Roman laws were thus to some extent operative in the California where John August Sutter maintained his fort in the early 1840s, a California then part of Mexico, and they seemed well suited to the needs and the sense of justice of squatter gold miners who rushed by the thousands to the newly acquired United States territory in 1849, after those stupendous discoveries at Sutter's Mill on the American. It was out of litigation involving these miners that United States courts first recognized the doctrine of prior appropriation. As interpreted by the courts in those early cases, the doctrine had three basic elements: first, the prior right of discovery; second, the retention of this right by exercise of it; and, third, the forfeiture of the right by failure to exercise it. Applied to miners, the doctrine insured the right to divert streams for mining purposes. Applied to agriculture later on, it insured the right to divert water for irrigation purposes.

But in California—and later in the Plain States—this rule of prior appropriation, this law out of warm dry Southern climates, met head on a wholly different kind of water law, originated in the cool and humid North. This was the famed riparian doctrine of English common law.

It had developed, of course, under conditions vastly different from those which prevail through most of the Mediterranean world and the American West. It had developed in a land with an abundance of water and which therefore faced no necessity for extensive stream diversions to irrigate agricultural lands. In terms of their uses, English streams were regarded as sources of drinking water; as sources of water power; as conveyors of commerce (you'll recall the royal protest in 1372 that excessive dumping interfered with navigation up the Thames); as areas of sewage disposal; and as areas of recreation (punting and fishing have ever been favorite pastimes of Englishmen). In an environment not overpopulated, as England was not when her basic laws developed, none of these uses is such that its exercise upstream must deny absolutely its exercise downstream. The water which goes over dams and turns the wheels of industry is not thereby affected in quantity or quality. Boating or fishing do nothing to injure a stream. This leaves such matters as waste disposal and the use of water for livestock and domestic purposes to be

cared for, and the English common law did so by ruling that
the owner of riparian land—that is, land contiguous or abutting
upon a natural stream—is entitled to have the stream flow by or
through his land undiminished in quantity, except for domestic
and livestock uses, and unchanged in quality.

Explains a report to the governor of Kansas in 1944, entitled
"The Appropriation of Water for Beneficial Purposes":[1]

Under the common-law doctrine the right to use stream water is regarded as real property and entitled to protection to the same extent as
other property. . . . [It] arises by operation of law as an incident of
the ownership of land, of which the right is an appurtenance. . . .
The right to the use of water from watercourses by contiguous landowners results solely by reason of location, and regardless of relative
productive capacities of such lands or uses. The right attaches to the
land at the time such land passes to private ownership. It is coequal
with the right of every other riparian owner on the stream regardless
of the relative dates on which the several tracts passed into private
ownership.

This gives an idea of what you're up against when lawyers "interpret" doubtful laws. It is composed in a prose style having as
its basic motive, one suspects, a desire for further lucrative litigation. (What, for instance, does "contiguous" landowners mean?
Are the *owners* contiguous, or is their *land* contiguous? Or does
our lawyer friend mean that the land is in actual contact with the
watercourse?) But you may be able to perceive, through a muddy
stream of words, that water rights, under English common law,
need not be exercised in order to be retained. Such rights are not
created by use nor forfeited by non-use.

It is a doctrine neatly consistent with the English soil and
climate. It is no less consistent with the historic English character.

[1]Subtitled "A Report to the Governor on Historic, Physical and Legal
Aspects of the Problem in Kansas," prepared by a committee appointed
by the governor to investigate these matters.

It mirrors a typically Protestant-capitalist conception of private property as the basic element of justice and freedom, and of freedom itself as a *form* of property, a private possession of the individual person rather than a function of organized groups. Liberty, so conceived, is quite largely definable in negative terms: it is an absence of restraints upon the individual, a freedom *from* external compulsions, an insurance against invasions of privacy. And this being true, the common law with its riparian doctrine suffered no sea change as it crossed the Atlantic with the Pilgrim Fathers. Its rather atomistic individualism was embraced without question by men whose very voyage was a protest against government regulations, and it found on the Eastern seaboard a climate which, if more severe than England's, was no less congenial to water laws that assumed an abundant water supply. The New Englanders need make no greater or different demands on their rivers than their forefathers across the seas had done.

But when in the 1850s a later generation of Puritans were swept westward to Bleeding Kansas on a tide of Abolitionist sentiment, the riparian doctrine which they carried with them ran into difficulties—the same difficulties California was experiencing as she sought to maintain the riparian and appropriation doctrines side by side. In 1855 the first territorial legislature of Kansas adopted the common law of England, and in the 1860s the state legislature reaffirmed it. In Nebraska the common law was not included among provisions of the state constitution but was almost immediately adopted by the legislature. And for the first few years, when rivers were still used primarily for navigation and the turning of water wheels, court decisions sustained and even strengthened the riparian doctrine. In the 1870s, however, the tides of immigration swept out onto the High Plains, and there began the long and painful process of adjusting written laws to physical realities.

Here was a land of little rain, of low water tables, and of

shallow streams which sometimes sank out of sight in their sandy beds. Here water was so precious that individuals could no longer be independent of one another in their use of it. Raw sewage disposal in streams of small and intermittent flow inevitably created public nuisances, if not dangers downstream. Irrigation upstream might prevent irrigation, or other water uses, downstream. Even domestic and livestock uses of a stream by one man might deny such uses to his downstream neighbors. In other words, streams could no longer be neatly divided into segments of private property; the equitable requirement on which such rights rested—namely, that the stream must flow from one riparian "owner" to another without diminution in quantity or quality—was impossible.

So bit by bit, in court case after court case, the riparian doctrine was modified until at last, by legislative action in both Nebraska and Kansas, it was frankly rejected and replaced by the doctrine of prior appropriation. Colorado, the third state involved in the Kansas River Basin, escaped many of these difficulties by adopting the appropriation doctrine to begin with, making it a part of the state constitution.

5

An Emerging Concept: The Watershed as Organism   This shift from the riparian doctrine to that of prior appropriation removed a principal legal obstacle to the maximum "best" development of available water supplies. In subhumid areas, such development requires community action. Irrigation requires that reservoirs and diversion dams be built, and systems of canals. Sanitary sewage disposal often requires that sewage-treatment plants be built. In drought years, as individual wells go dry, even the supply of water to farmers for household or livestock use may become a community endeavor. Hence, so far as water use is concerned, "freedom" can no longer be meaningfully defined in terms of exclusive individual "rights." It becomes a group concern, a function of community action, and can be maintained only through practical democratic planning in which the watershed as a whole is considered.

Thus we return to the lessons suggested by our blurred snapshots from history—namely, that the river is an organic element of a watershed. Its uses, its problems are all interrelated, being aspects of the total watershed as problem; and they must be considered in terms of the organic whole. Any attempt to solve piecemeal the problems of stream pollution, of irrigation, of flood control, of downstream navigation, of recreational development —any attempt to solve these as though they were *separate* problems is doomed, by the law of nature, to ultimate failure. . . .

It has been remarked in passing that we Americans, like the imperial Romans, are a remarkably unphilosophical race. Justly proud of our great technical and administrative abilities, we dislike to be reminded that engineering, and administration, and business enterprise have no purpose or value in themselves but are means to ends which *are* purposes and values: and in consequence we are much better at building big dams, for example, than we are at deciding whether or not those dams *ought* to be built. In other words, we're "practical" men—impatient of "mere" theory and of large generalizations. We distrust those abstractions which are the materials of free speculation, and regard metaphysics as useless if not actually "silly."

In view of this attitude it is interesting to note a parallel, curious and perhaps significant, between the *kind* of thinking done by contemporary philosophers as they concern themselves with abstract problems of permanence and change, and the kind forced upon our more advanced engineers as they concern themselves with concrete problems of river development. The most abstract metaphysics and the most practical experience seem here to point in the same direction; they seem to lead to precisely analogous conclusions.

To the metaphysician the river generally presents itself as metaphor. "You cannot step twice into the same river," wrote Heraclitus of Ephesus some 500 years before Christ—and philosophers ever since have used the river as a symbol of Change, of Flowing Time, of a continuous flux of reality. As the metaphor is extended, the solid land through which the river flows becomes a symbol of the Permanent, the static element by which change is measured, the Eternal which is out of Time altogether. Almost the whole of modern philosophy, up until very recent times, can be divided into two seemingly hostile camps by virtue of the relative emphasis given to one or the other of these two polar concepts.

Those who stress the river, regarding Change as the essence of reality, are generally mystics of one sort or another. They doubt the accuracy of logic as a guide to ultimate truths, because the logical intelligence "stops the flow" of reality and divides it into artificial static segments. More accurate in the realm of ultimates, they assert, is intuition, operating in flashes of *felt* truth which stimulate and provide the substance of all creative thought. Such philosophy is sympathetic to theology; it is not uncompromisingly averse to assigning to acts of Faith a status "superior" to acts of Reason. On the other hand, those philosophers who stress the land—the permanent, the solid, the eternal—are generally rationalists and, quite often, materialists of one sort or another. They regard logic operating on sense-experience as the best test of truth, if not the only guide to it; they assert the feelings to be very dangerous guides indeed; and they sometimes lead the way toward an arid intellectualism, a realm of cold logic utterly devoid of living values.

Implicit here are the oppositions which so tragically divide our world. Here, in an age which goes to extremes, are implied the savage wars of religion vs. science in education, of emotion vs. intellect in the individual soul, of fascism vs. communism in European politics, of the mysticism of the East vs. the intellectualism of the West in the new battle for the world. Implicit, too, is a recognition of the goal toward which we must proceed if we are to survive as a world civilization. Our great problem is one of finding common denominators of the extremes and thus modifying them; our ultimate goal is an organic unity of seeming oppositions by which they are recognized as separate aspects of a single reality in so far as they have any validity at all. Hence we find emerging, as the most representative philosophic efforts of our time, systems of synthesis and organism. F. S. C. Northrop writes a symptomatic book entitled *The Meeting of East and West*, in which his whole purpose is to fuse the "aesthetic component" of the East with the "theoretic component" of the West to form a "higher" synthesis. And A. N. Whitehead, perhaps the most powerful philosophic mind of the century, fuses the mystical and logical approaches to reality in what he calls "the philosophy of organism."

To the engineer, the river presents itself as a practical problem. It is an obstacle to be bridged, a channel to be dredged, a potential flood to be checked, a source of water to be developed for industrial and agricultural and sanitation uses. But here, too, we find an extension of the original proposition. The land becomes involved with the river. And here, too, in the realm of the concrete and particular, we find a sharp division between those who place their major emphasis on the flowing river and those who most emphasize the solid land which the river drains. Oppositions arise between those primarily concerned with flood control and navigation and those primarily concerned with agricultural irrigation—the former thinking primarily of the river as problem and the latter thinking primarily of the land as problem. In terms of flood control itself, there are oppositions between those who emphasize land use (i.e., upstream soil and water conservation) and those who emphasize river development (i.e., big dams downstream). It is interesting to note Bernard DeVoto, in *Harper's* magazine, applying the very language of our philosophic discussion to the above engineering oppositions. Proponents of our present big dam program in the Missouri Valley are, he says, practicing "engineering mysticism."

But the point is that a solution to this practical problem of land vs. water seems, as I've said, precisely analogous to the solution of the abstract problem of permanence vs. change. It, too, requires the discovery of a common denominator of the extremes—a physical one, this time. It requires a concrete realization that the seemingly different, and opposed, elements are actually organically linked. This being so, an exponent of pure *a priori* reasoning might expect to find a continuous physical reality joining land and river, blurring out of existence any sharp distinction between the two—and, sure enough, this physical reality does exist. It is water, the element common to both river and land. Indeed, from one point of view, the only difference between river and land is the proportion of water to solid materials, the river having a higher percentage of water per unit volume—and this difference is reduced as stream turbidity increases. The Missouri River, for example, was accurately described by Father Membre as "clear mud," and a contemporary writer[1] has described it as in reality three rivers—one of water, one of silt, and one of sediment.

Russell Lord, in an article recently published in *The Land,* sums up our conclusion as follows:

"We like to think of 'bodies of land' and 'bodies of water' as though they were separate, but they are not. There is really no such thing as dry land anywhere. A web of water, aboveground and underground, encircles the Earth, and thus, visibly and

[1] Rufus Terral, *The Missouri Valley*. New Haven: Yale University Press, 1947. Page 91.

invisibly, the ends of the Earth and all forms of life are linked."

The conclusion has clear practical implications. It implies that ground and surface water must be considered as a single element and used in accordance with a single water policy, particularly in such subhumid areas as the Great Plains. This point was made by the report of the governor of Kansas, previously quoted,[2] "The Appropriation of Water for Beneficial Purposes." Says the report (pages 11 and 16):

The source of all the surface and ground water supplies in the State is the rain which falls on the land. A portion of the rain runs off directly into the streams, constituting the more fluctuating part of the stream flow. Another portion, entering and percolating through the soil, joins the water table and starts moving slowly but continuously toward an outlet into some stream, the flow of which it helps to maintain. Such water constitutes the more regular and stable part of the stream flow. . . . The Committee feels compelled[3] . . . to point out that the source of both water in streams and in . . . underground reservoirs is the same; that water used from one is not available for use from the other; that the State cannot wisely have a system of water rights for surface water and none for ground water or one system for surface water and another for ground water if there is to be orderly development of the water resources of the State.

[2]On page 74.

[3]This use of the term "compelled" might be taken to have a psychological significance. Certainly the typically American mind seems to resist as far as possible the pressures toward the kind of thinking which the author of our quotation is doing.

Polluted Waters **IV**

1

Rivers Alive—but Sick   Consider, for a moment, the *intimacy* of water. Herman Melville hinted of it in the opening pages of his *Moby Dick* as he told why his Ishmael went periodically down to the sea in ships.

"Say, you are in the country; in some high land of lakes," wrote Melville. "Take almost any path you please, and ten to one it carries you down in a dale, and leaves you there by a pool in the stream. There is magic in it. Let the most absent-minded of men be plunged in his deepest reveries—stand that man on his legs, set his feet a-going, and he will infallibly lead you to water, if water there be in all that region."

What is this instinctual magic by which men are drawn to water, even though they be not athirst? Why do we so often choose as our seat of contemplation the bank of a lake or stream? And what is it drives us out in boats, with or without a fishing rod, and makes of swimming the most joyous of solitary exercises? Could it be the attraction of like to like?

Perhaps. For we ourselves are mostly water, physically speaking. "Even the Archbishop of Canterbury comprises 59 per cent of water," writes Sir Arthur Shipley in his book entitled *Life*, though the proportion varies from tissue to tissue in the Archbishop, as in ourselves. Blood, of course, is more than nine tenths water. Our kidneys are sometimes as much as 82 per cent water. The average muscle is 75 per cent water. Liver is 69 per cent water. Even our bones, which we incline to think of as dry and solid lime, are in their living state 22 per cent water. The vital interior of all cells is fluid, consisting largely of solutions of various substances in water, and through our perspiration, our moist breaths, and our excretions water is continually being lost from our bodies. Every year we replace the loss by pouring down our gullets approximately five times our own weight of water. About 6,500 gallons will have poured through our systems by the time we die, if our life span is normal—and that span will abruptly end if we are cut off, for more than a very few days, from a supply of drinkable water. It is thus no fanciful metaphor which describes man's life as a flowing stream, or describes his body as a liquid flux contained by banks and strewn with shoals of water-permeated tissue.

Like to like! Observe a mountain brook sparkling in sunlight, whispering past grassy banks, laughing softly as it leaps the white stones of a rapid, roaring with laughter as it plunges down a fall. Observe a wilderness river in wooded country, more sedately flowing, faintly stained a reddish-brown with leaf mold, but remaining crystal-clear nonetheless and reflecting with refreshing candor all the moods of sky. Such brooks and rivers seem alive, and in a sense they *are* alive. They breathe air. They perspire, yielding moisture to the air. They require good water to drink if they are to remain strong and healthy. Though they are now sparkling with good health, they are vulnerable to disease, and the disease may be fatal, transforming them into ugly stinking corpses. What strange horror we then feel, looking down upon a dead body of water! It is as though a friend had died—and we had killed him!

Nor are such feelings of guilt unjustified. Almost always the disease of the river is man, or the works of man. Too many human beings crowded upon the river are like too many hostile germs crowded upon a blood stream, spewing poisons into a vital flux more rapidly than the flux can overcome them. Civilization can prevent this, but, alas, it has not often done so. More often it has done just the opposite. Generally speaking, our industrialized cities and mechanized farms have been ministering to our desires at the expense of our natural environment, killing the latter element by element, and at an increasing tempo. Our mills digest whole forests; our plows lay bare vast slopes of soil; our mines probe the mineral guts of the earth; our factories hugely mold dead stuff into the shapes, the many thousand shapes, of our wish. And the immense wastes of these immense labors we callously thrust down the throats of our rivers. The rivers choke on them.

Consider how a river may die! Think of it now, not as a living entity, but as a complex of living entities, a vital system sustaining in its bosom myriad forms of life which are balanced one against another in much the same way as life is balanced on the (relatively) dry land. Think of it, to begin with, as a habitat of fishes—for of all the life forms of the river, these are the most obvious to man's eyes and the most appealing to his interests.

Fish must breathe. Like men (each of whom had once the shape of a fish in his mother's womb, gill slit and all), fish maintain their vital energies by a slow burning of tissues, a process of oxidation; and since carbon is the chief substance oxidized, fish, like men, exhale chiefly carbon dioxide. They must, then, have oxygen. It might seem that this could present no problem to creatures immersed in H_2O, a substance made up of one part oxygen to every two parts hydrogen. But water is a toughly integrated substance: breaking the link between the H_2 and the O requires a much more elaborate chemistry than any fish is capable of: so the fish must breathe in "free" (that is, uncombined) oxygen, just as men do. This oxygen is dissolved in the water, whence it has been absorbed from the air. Up to 9.17 parts of oxygen per million by weight may be so dissolved at 20 degrees C., and a trout needs, at the very least, 5 parts per million. A trout won't flourish, however, if less than 7 parts per million are present, while a mud catfish or a carp may do very well on half that amount. It is thus obvious that anything which affects the oxygen supply of a stream affects the character of the fish life of that stream, and any drastic reduction of the former must mean a reduction of the latter. One thing which affects oxygen supply, incidentally, is temperature. The colder the water, the more oxygen it can hold, other things being equal, and this is one reason why trout (the athletes of the piscatorial world) are found in mountain streams but *not* in the rivers of the Kansas Basin.

Not only must fish breathe; they must also eat. Otherwise they have nothing to oxidize. And what do they eat? They feed a great deal on each other, of course, big fishes swallowing little ones with a distressing lack of fastidiousness. They feed on insects which ride the surface of the water and tiny crustaceans which float in it. They feed on random bits of animal life which grow into the stream or are washed into it—bristle worms, for example, which look like earthworms and often breed in vast quantities in the oozy beds of slow-flowing rivers. But ultimately fish, like other animals, depend for food upon vegetable life: organisms which can feed directly on mineral elements, synthesizing organic compounds out of inorganic materials. (In the process, carbon dioxide is absorbed and free oxygen expelled, thus helping to maintain or increase the dissolved oxygen content of the river.) There is a good deal of this kind of life in the ordinary river's vital system, much of it invisible to the naked eye. The amount varies inversely with stream flow—rapid streams have relatively little—and directly with light and temperature, up to a certain point. Photosynthesis, the process by which chlorophyll (the green stuff of plants) employs light energy in the compounding of organic tissues, cannot of course take place at all if sufficient light is not present.

Further, fish have certain standards of cleanliness. In part these are imposed by the manner in which a fish breathes. Having no nose, the fish must breathe through its mouth, the first step being the opening of that mouth and the closing of the gill covers. This done, the mouth is shut, the gill covers opened, and the mouthful of water squirted through the gill slits past delicate filaments which are chock-full of tiny blood vessels. These absorb free oxygen from the water directly into the blood stream. Obviously the suspended solid material in a notably dirty stream may injure the gill filaments; it may even clog the gill openings; and the result in either case may be that the poor fish chokes to death. This purely mechanical requirement of cleanliness is by no means the only one imposed by the fish's nature, however. Fish may seem to us remarkably unfinicky in their eating habits; the range of their food may seem to us both queer and wide. But fish which eat filth taste of filth when we eat them, and they cannot eat just any old thing. They *can* be poisoned. Sad and all too frequent are the occasions when some industrial plant suddenly dumps a large amount of chemical waste into a river and thereby kills every fish in it for miles downstream.

Keeping the above facts in mind, we can define almost the whole nature of stream pollution in fishy terms.

Consider, first, the effects of sewage disposal on dissolved oxygen content. All along the lower reaches of the Kaw, to take one example, are towns and cities which pour into the river their wastes: the excretions of human bodies, the refuse of food-processing plants, and waters fouled by their use in industrial processes. For the most part these wastes are unstable organic compounds which have not been treated in sewage plants. The river must digest them. And how does the river do so? It dissolves that which is soluble; it breaks into fine pieces loosely integrated but insoluble materials, holding these in suspension; and it supplies the oxygen needed by the millions of microorganisms which, feeding on the sewage, transform it into a sludge no more offensive and far more fertile than ordinary topsoil. The whole process consumes oxygen. Wherever the river is overloaded with sewage, as it is along some miles of the Kaw and its tributaries, the oxygen supply is so reduced that many of what the sportsman regards as the "best" fish cannot survive at all.

Consider, second, the effects of solid materials on the river's light economy. As turbidity increases, light penetration decreases. Some years ago the Bureau of Fisheries made studies at hundreds of points on streams of the Mississippi, Ohio, and Missouri river systems, studies which included more than 5,000 determinations of light penetration.[1] It was found that light of a certain intensity penetrated a clear mountain stream to depths of 50,000 millimeters, whereas that same light penetrated the Missouri River to a depth of only 84 millimeters. Turbidity, primarily composed of erosion silt but augmented by urban wastes, made the difference.

[1] Reported in U. S. Department of Commerce, Bureau of Fisheries Circular No. 7, 1931.

Inevitably this reduction in light means a reduction in populations of the better fish. Every fisherman knows that game fish won't bite when the stream is muddied by high water, and he therefore avoids the stream at such times. If the stream is permanently muddied, the game fish retire or die out altogether. The whole character of the river as a vital system is changed when its waters grow opaque, and involved in the change is a reduction of the river's capacity to clean up the messes dumped into it: the microorganisms which release oxygen through photosynthesis cannot live without light, and the oxygen they would release is needed for the digestion of organic wastes. All manner of evil may safely thrive in darkness. The river becomes poisonous.

Consider, third, how the fish's food supply and its nests and spawning grounds are ruined as the waters grow turbid. As shifting blankets of debris cover the bottoms of streams they smother out the organisms which normally live there and on which fish normally feed. The bed of a river like the Kaw or the Missouri is itself a thickly flowing syrup: it is a loose mass of sediment which pours sluggishly downstream, pausing when the river is low, accelerating when the river is high, but always denying to fish their proper homes and a fit place to lay their eggs. Moreover, "silt tends to precipitate chemical wastes, oils, and pulps dumped into streams," writes M. M. Ellis,[2] "and decomposition of these substances decreases the amount of essential oxygen available at the bottom of the stream."

Thus does stream pollution manifest itself in fishy terms. Thus may the decline in fish life measure the sickness of rivers. What is injurious to fish is, in this case and generally speaking, injurious to men and whatever we do to cure the stream for our own sakes will largely restore it as a habitat for fishes. So far, the curative efforts have been meager indeed compared to the river-sickness

[2]In an article, "Erosion Silt as a Factor in Aquatic Environments," *Ecology*, Vol. 17, 1936.

we have produced. For the most part we've treated (and inadequately) the symptoms rather than the causes of the disease.

Stand for a few moments on the bank of the Kaw at Kansas City when the river flow is normal. Watch the process of river infection. It is appalling. The earth on which the city stands is honeycombed with tubes, and into them is rejected that which stinks and festers. Small tubes feed into larger ones, and these into still larger ones, until the largest are reached. The largest go down to the edge of the river, beneath our feet, and spew out like so many anal openings their collected filth. From the bank you can watch greasy stains, varicolored and with globules of garbage and other solid stuff in them, streaming and spreading from each opening down and across water already brown with mud. Inorganic wastes mingle with organic ones. Here is a yellow streak of sulphur, there is a green streak of copper, beyond is a black streak of mineral oil which, as it spreads, becomes rainbow-hued. But bearing all these, and spreading over increasing portions of the river surface, is the film of grease. It has, alas, a certain odor.

Here we see with immediate vision what happens when the river, a vital system, is treated mechanically, as though it were a fluid wastebasket of unlimited capacity. We sense the living stream's sick rebellion against such mechanism. It suffers from indigestion, from acute constipation, and we ourselves are revolted by it. We feel *personally* outraged. We deplore the spectacle from the watery depths of our beings. . . .

2

Diagnosis: Method and Data   So far in this essay we have been looking at the river and its pollution pretty much as artists might, defining our outward vision in terms of an inward response to it.

As artists—and each natural man *is* in this sense an artist—we are concerned with the concrete entirety of things. Artistic method, if so spontaneous a process may be called a "method," is one of *feeling* one's self into the vital heart of whatever is looked upon, realizing each object in its "unanalyzable unity." The way of art toward the outer world is contemplative, and intuitive, and determined by living values. Thus for the artist green boughs are gay, naked boughs are sad, the river rolls proudly or sullenly broods, and the gray hardness of stones is ungrateful. Our own Kaw River seemed sullen to us as we watched it from the banks of Kansas City. It seemed dangerously so as it poured its poisoned substance into the broad Missouri. . . .

But now we must look at the river, not as artists, but as scientists. This is a very different way; it is more a method than a process.

The scientist *as* scientist is not concerned with the concrete entirety of things, but with their schematic outlines—and these are invariably patterns of possible action upon the object under investigation. His *ultimate* goal is not "mere" understanding, not the "meaning" or "truth" or "value" which aesthetic contemplation uncovers; rather, his goal is a definite, practical design for action. In so far as he does seek to understand, it is (ultimately) in order to act,[1] and by his methods he can understand *only* that which is relevant to action. Indeed, he goes to great lengths to rule out "irrelevant" values, imposing a rigorous censorship on his natural impulses to insure that his discoveries are precisely limited concepts on which practical programs may be based. The scientist, then, far from looking upon objects as "unanalyzable unities,"

[1]This is Henri Bergson's conception, of course, and it is less true of "pure" than of "applied" science, it seems to me. The chief difference between the two is that in applied science the desired useful end is given at the outset of an investigation, whereas the pure scientist has a less precise goal and hence has more freedom to indulge his aesthetic tastes and his play instinct.

regards them as bundles of relations, and the first step of his investigation is a disintegrative one. He analyzes the whole into its parts, classifying the latter in specific categories whose basic determination (though this is not often realized) is use-value.

Of this procedure, the pollution investigation of the Kansas River system completed a few years ago is an almost perfect example. The survey was conducted by Kansas and Nebraska, working co-operatively with three Federal agencies. Its findings were published by the U. S. Public Health Service in co-operation with the Kansas State Board of Health, the Nebraska State Department of Health, the U. S. Corps of Engineers, and the U. S. Bureau of Reclamation.[2] Those scientists engaged in it looked upon the river with a measuring eye. They were concerned to see the Kaw and its tributaries not as a total flowing reality but as a succession of static moments, each moment being precisely located in the stream and each presenting to their trained vision a measurable pattern of pollution.

The *first* step of these scientists was to "freeze" the river into 4,310 water samples, gathered with a uniform precision at predetermined points: calibrated jars on long chains were lowered from bridges, boats, or banks to precisely assigned depths, and exact temperatures were taken. The *second* step was to analyze these samples into 34,500 separate laboratory determinations, chemical and bacteriological, the routine analyses being supplemented by special studies of chlorides in streams and of dissolved oxygen. The *third* step was to combine the individual patterns of pollution thus revealed into an over-all pattern for the watershed.

[2] The survey resulted from a Memorandum of Understanding among these agencies, effective October 17, 1947, and was initiated that same autumn. The report of the investigation was issued in mimeographed form in June 1949 by the Federal Security Agency, Public Health Service, under the title "Kansas River Basin Water Pollution Investigation."

The latter became a pattern for action. It indicated what should be done to reduce pollution and so restore to our streams some of their former health and beauty.

The yardsticks used to measure pollution in this investigation were various and ingenious—and so interesting to me personally that, at the risk of boring readers with technical detail, I'm going to tell about them. I think I may justify doing so by saying that a study of them has been useful to my own effort to learn how to think about a river; it may therefore be useful to others. From it I've gained something of the *feel* of the technician's work and a heightened appreciation of that work's value, and of the uses of highly specialized technical minds, in river development. I've also derived, I think, a clearer realization of how and why it is that the technical mind—so valuable, so indispensable to successful river development—may often be incapacitated for the kind of top-level river-policy-making we now so badly need. It is easy to lose sight of the forest when individual trees are so interesting.

The analytical tests in the Kansas water-pollution investigation were made in three laboratories—and it might be thought that these laboratory tests would be designed to measure *directly* the dangerous infections of the river: for example, the number of typhoid germs present per unit volume at given points. Such tests can be made. But they are expensive of time and materials, and other tests, in which infection is measured indirectly, are sufficiently accurate. Hence the latter were employed in this investigation. Generally speaking, factors which condition infection and indicate pollution were measured rather than the infection and pollution themselves. Most of these factors have been spoken of in our fish-eye view of the river.

We've spoken, for instance, of dissolved oxygen content and of its importance to the good health of the stream. One of the routine laboratory tests measured the amount of dissolved oxygen present, comparing this with the amount (9.17 p.p.m. at 20 de-

grees C.) which water holds when saturated. More than 9.17
p.p.m. are occasionally found, incidentally: the stream may be
"supersaturated" in the presence of an abundance of algae or
other plant life.

Closely associated with this test was one for biochemical
oxygen demand (B.O.D.), an ingenious indicator of organic
pollution in that it measures the amount of oxygen required to
oxidize the unstable organic compounds that are present. After
the amount of dissolved oxygen has been measured, portions of
the sample are sealed in test tubes and held for five days at 20
degrees C. At the end of that time the amount of oxygen is again
measured, the difference representing the amount used by digesting organisms in their oxidation processes. In actual practice the
test is by no means as simple and easy as our description of it
may imply: it is, indeed, very delicate and sensitive, requiring
experienced skill for its accurate use: but the basic procedure is
as we've indicated, and the results are highly informative. To
interpret them, it is necessary to remember that the capacity of
a stream to "breathe in" oxygen varies inversely with temperature: the higher the temperature, the less oxygen, other things
being equal. This fact, combined with the fact that the rate of
biochemical oxidation increases with temperature, indicates that
the most critical pollution conditions, so far as oxygen is concerned, are likely to occur in the summer months, when normally
temperatures are high in our basin and stream flows are low.
(Equally severe conditions occur during the winter when the
streams are covered with ice and normal reoxygenation cannot
take place.) The oxygen demand is, of course, considered in
relation to the amount of dissolved oxygen present. Whenever
and wherever the demand is greater than the supply the river is
dangerously ill.

These B.O.D. figures may be used to determine what are called
"population equivalents," a convenient statistical language for

expressing degrees of pollution. This becomes possible because the average composition of domestic sewage is fairly constant. In America the average is 54 grams of B.O.D. per capita daily— which is to say that each person, on the average, commits to the toilet each day organic wastes requiring 54 grams of oxygen for digestion. (The amount tends to vary with the wealth of the person: the richer he is, the more putrescent matter he contributes —a fact which might tempt a contemporary Hugo into flights of metaphor dangerous to him, anti-Red hysteria being what it is.) The actual B.O.D. found in streams, however, is higher than it would be if domestic sewage were the only source of pollution. Analysis may reveal, for example, that sewage from a community of 1,000 persons contains 74 grams per capita daily of B.O.D. instead of the average 54. Simple arithmetic translates the larger figure into a population equivalent for the community of approximately 1,400 persons.

A third routine test of Kansas Basin samples was a measurement of turbidity, the suspended solid material which thickens and renders opaque the waters of the stream. Results were expressed in p.p.m. by weight—and as our fish-eye view would lead us to expect, a correlation was quite generally found between B.O.D. values, high and low stream stages, and p.p.m. of suspended solids. But of more immediate significance to sanitary engineers were the results of a fourth routine test, in which the "most probable number" (M.P.N.) of microorganisms of the coliform group was determined. Since these organisms occur in very small numbers in a natural stream but are discharged in vast quantities in human feces, their presence in any considerable amount at normal flows indicates domestic sewage pollution. At high flows, the number of coliforms is swelled by runoff from barnyards—for these microorganisms are present in the intestinal tracts of all warm-blooded animals.

Routine tests were also made for alkalinity, measured in terms of quantity (p.p.m.) and intensity (pH values).[3] The alkalinity of water generally indicates that carbonates, bicarbonates, and hydroxides are present. Associated with these tests were those for chlorides, whose entrance into streams creates a type of pollution particularly important and dangerous in our basin. We shall return to it later on. Common table salt, as you know, is composed of one part sodium to one part chlorine, and the very name of the Saline River indicates a natural pollution with this substance. The natural pollution may be augmented by a careless disposal of oil-field wastes, and our investigators were concerned to discover the extent of this latter damage.

Such general characteristics of the streams as temperature, color, taste, odor, and flow in cubic feet per second past sampling points were also measured in the investigation. Special studies were made of some of the industries and sewage plants. When the results of all these studies were put together in comprehensive tables (listed in columns of figures, they added up to well over 100 full pages of small type), trained eyes could discern in them the nature and geographic pattern of pollution in this basin. And when these were considered in conjunction with the distribution of population and industry, and with the sources of municipal water supplies, the specific needs of pollution control became evident. Suffice it here to say that the survey revealed the need for more pollution-abatement activity.

The river's capacity for self-purification—that is, its ability to digest the wastes poured into it—was of course carefully studied, for it directly influences decisions as to the kind and amount of pollution control. In general, the main streams of our basin were

[3]pH is the negative logarithm of the hydrogen ion concentration. Liquid whose pH value is 7.0 is "neutral"—i.e., neither acid nor alkaline. If it tests below 7.0 it is acid, and if above it is alkaline, the intensity increasing (up to a limit) with the difference between the test value and the neutral point.

found to have somewhat higher digestive capacities than had been anticipated. The rate at which our streams use up dissolved oxygen in the digestion of organic pollutions is about what the scientists had expected. "Deoxygenation," this is called. But the ability of the stream to "soak up" oxygen ("reoxygenation") was somewhat greater than scientists had expected. Probably this higher rate is due in part to the climatic characteristics of the region—to the fact that we have so much bright sunshine, which encourages algae and other plant organisms (particularly in warm and sluggish streams) to grow and multiply, releasing oxygen through photosynthesis. Certainly what is called "surface reaeration," whereby air is physically lapped up by the surface of the stream, is not as high in our basin as it is in mountainous regions where there are many rapids and waterfalls and the streams run swift and cool. So algae must be given much of the credit for the fact that Kansas-system streams contain, on the average, somewhat more than the 5 p.p.m. of dissolved oxygen which constitute the minimum requirement for a balanced aquatic life.

But the self-purification ability of our streams varies greatly. It varies from place to place and from time to time. It varies with stream stage, for one thing. At higher stream flows, the dissolved oxygen content is actually less than might be expected, primarily because turbidity (mostly erosion silt) and organic pollution both go up as the water rises. Soil is washed from fields into streams in periods of high runoff, and farmyards and other areas of land surface bearing organic wastes are scoured. Turbidity, as we've pointed out, means a decrease in light penetration, and this means a decrease in algae. Increased organic pollution, indicated by a higher B.O.D. and higher coliform numbers, means an increase in deoxygenation rates. Result: a more dangerous pollution of the stream. Here you may perceive a direct connection between the problems of pollution control and flood control. As peak stream flows are reduced by dams, and as streams are "ponded" in reservoirs, the total pollution load may be reduced and the growth of algae increased. On the other hand, "ponding" means a reduction in atmospheric aeration; sluggish or still waters do not lap up air as rapidly or in as great quantities as do free-flowing streams.

There becomes evident, here, the need for integrated river development. Otherwise, from the standpoint of pollution control, the control of floods through dams and reservoirs may be no unmixed blessing in our basin, and irrigation developments may be a positive evil.

In the first place, algae growths, valuable within limits, may be encouraged beyond those limits in impounded waters. Released downstream, such excessive growths may mean an increase in unpleasant tastes and odors which must be removed by water treatment in those municipalities drawing their drinking water from streams. Such tastes and odors, difficult and expensive to remove in even the most efficient plants, have long presented one of the most vexing problems faced by waterworks engineers in our basin. Any increase in them will be decidedly unwelcomed.

In the second place, the Tuttle Creek Reservoir on the Big Blue (see map), a flood-control project for which congressional appropriation has been made, may create special water-supply and pollution-control problems at Marysville, Kansas. This town of 4,000 draws its water supply from the Blue and discharges raw sewage into the Blue. If the final design of the Tuttle Creek Reservoir were such that the Blue was "surcharged" to Marysville, the town's raw sewage would be backed up into the water supply. As we shall emphasize later, Marysville should not be discharging raw sewage into the river, nor should any other town; a sewage-treatment plant should and will be built. But even so, new arrangements for both drinking water and sewage disposal—probably a relocation of water-intake and sewage-discharge pipes—

would be needed if the "high pool stage" indicated on a Corps of Engineers map, issued in March of 1947, were actually developed for Tuttle Creek.

In the third place, and still more serious in terms of pollution control, are the consequences of any drastic reduction of flows in the main stem of the Kaw as a result of irrigation diversions from the Republican River below the Harlan County Dam (see map). Just in general, and other things being equal, a stream's ability to digest wastes varies directly with the size of its normal flows. For this reason alone, any great reduction of minimum flows, and average flows, means that municipalities will have to spend more money on sewage treatment in order to maintain or restore the health of the river. But the problem for the Kaw's main stem is further complicated by the fact that low-mineral-content water from the Republican dilutes the waters from the Smoky Hill system where the main stem forms at Junction City, and the latter waters have what sanitary engineers call "poor mineral quality." As we've pointed out, the very name of the Saline River indicates a natural pollution with sodium chloride and other salts, and this pollution can be augmented by oil-field waste disposals. Our point now is that any important reduction in the Republican's flow will have adverse effects on the quality of the river below Junction City. Since chlorides cannot be removed by water treatment, the downstream cities which draw water from the Kaw must dilute it with fresh water from wells.

All these problems are soluble, of course. But the difficulty and cost of their solution can be much reduced if they are properly anticipated in over-all basin plans. . . .

Let us now begin at the lower reaches of the Kansas system and move upstream, taking note of the salient features of the pollution problem as we proceed.

The sub-basin drained directly by the Kaw itself extends westward from Kansas City to Junction City and is by far the most heavily populated of all the sub-basins of the Kansas system. It contains thirty-eight municipalities, of which four are, for this region, considerable towns: Kansas City, Kansas, with 147,000 people;[4] Topeka with 87,000; Lawrence with 18,000; and Manhattan with 17,600. Of these four, two—Topeka and Lawrence —draw drinking water directly from the Kaw. Three other towns —Olathe with 5,000 people, Horton with 3,000, and Onaga with 900—draw their water from tributaries. The other municipalities draw their water from ground sources.

Not only is this the most heavily populated of all the sub-basins, it is also the most industrialized. The sewered population (the number of actual living people who commit their organic wastes to sewers) is approximately 270,000, but the amount of stream pollution produced (B.O.D.) is equivalent to a population of about 1,060,000. Subtract the first figure from the last and you find that a pollution population equivalent of 790,000 is contributed by industries. The pollution produced by the combination of domestic and industrial sewage is reduced by sewage-treatment plants to a sewered population equivalent of about 940,000 before being discharged into the stream. This reduction is not enough to maintain stream quality and insure public health. Even if Kansas City, at the Kaw's mouth, be excluded from consideration, sewage treatment remains inadequate. The sewered population equivalent connected to sewage-treatment plants amounts to 69 per cent of the total.

By far the most important contributors of organic wastes to the sub-basin streams are the food-processing industries: meat-packing plants, poultry-dressing stations, canneries, and creameries. These are concentrated on the banks of streams in order that they may use the flowing waters for the disposal of wastes. Kansas

[4]Based on estimates in Kansas State Board of Agriculture Bulletin, *Population of Kansas*, August 24, 1948.

City's world-famous packing industry, for example, stands on the natural flood plain of the Kaw and Missouri, and its contribution of organic wastes is far greater, just by itself, than that of the city's total population. The total population connected to sewers there is 103,000,[5] but the sewered population equivalent (all of it untreated) is 777,000! Domestic sewage, in other words, amounts to considerably less than one seventh of the total pollution which Kansas City consigns to the already overburdened Kaw. Here, of all places in the basin, the river is most foul. In our survey, those who sampled the river here noted "floating garbage, oil, and coarse sewage solids, all indicative of gross pollution"—and these visual evidences were more than confirmed by later laboratory tests for dissolved oxygen, coliforms, B.O.D., and so on.

Topeka, too, some eighty-two river miles upstream, has a considerable packing-plant and creamery industry. As early as 1885 the Kansas Board of Health was concerned about the state capital's river pollution. A report of the Board referred to the famous cry of a sacred singer of Israel, as recorded in the Bible: "Moah is my washpot": and suggested that Topeka could parallel this with "The Kaw is my washpot and my ice pond"—for in those days ice was cut from the river in winter. Polluted ice is no longer a major health problem, but in other respects the Kaw's pollution at Topeka has not, alas, improved. More than two thirds of the city's sewage goes raw into the river. Twenty miles downstream, Lawrence takes its water from that river, purifies it, drinks it, and flushes most of it back into the stream bearing domestic sewage and industrial wastes. Twenty miles below Lawrence's sewage

[5]This in itself is a distressingly significant figure, taken in conjunction with the fact that Kansas City's total population is around 147,000. It indicates that some 44,000 people in this modern city lack indoor plumbing facilities. This is nearly 30 per cent of the total population! There is a far more serious substandard housing problem than comfortably placed people like to admit, and it frankly worries the Kansas State Board of Health.

discharge lies the intake of the largest water-treatment plant in Kansas, that of the Sunflower Ordnance Works, which, though shut down after World War II, has recently been reactivated. And twenty miles below the Sunflower intake lies Kansas City. . . . You can see how pollution is compounded as populations and industrial concentrations increase.

Of the towns on small tributaries of the Kaw, Tonganoxie has contributed perhaps the most serious pollution problem. It was so serious, in fact, that the Kansas Board of Health was forced to take action in the interests of public health. Only 1,000 people live here, and they maintain a treatment plant for domestic sewage. Nevertheless, a pollution population equivalent of 3,580 goes untreated into Tonganoxie Creek, 3.1 miles above that stream's entrance into the Kaw. The major source of this pollution is a milk-processing plant whose wastes have gone untreated. (A treatment plant for these wastes has been planned, and construction may be under way by the time this book is published.)

The sub-basin drained by the Big Blue River has an over-all pollution problem much less serious than that along the main stem, but having the same general pattern. The population connected to sewers totals 87,000, while industrial wastes (mostly from food-processing plants) amount to a population equivalent of 40,200 people before treatment. There is some treatment, however. It cuts the total pollution from 127,200 to a little less than 74,000, in population equivalent terms. Fourteen of the 47 sewered municipalities in this sub-basin, having a sewered population equivalent of approximately 53,000, discharge raw sewage into the streams. Only three municipalities, however, draw their water from surface sources. Of these only Marysville, Kansas, draws from the Blue itself.

The most serious local pollution problem in this sub-basin is perhaps that of Hastings, Nebraska, a city of some 20,000 on the far reaches of the West Fork tributary of the Blue. This stream is so small that the discharged sewage below Hastings constitutes, in dry summer months, a substantial portion of the total flow. The result has been a serious public nuisance at various times and no small threat to public health. More sewage treatment is necessary, and Hastings plans to build new and expanded treatment facilities. Similar overloadings of small streams were encountered at Aurora, on Lincoln Creek in Nebraska, and at York, on Beaver Creek. At only twelve points in this sub-basin did investigators find the B.O.D. to be in excess of 5 p.p.m. Four of these points were below Hastings, three were below Aurora, and two were below York.

Thus we encounter a factor which is of relatively small importance to the pollution problem in the main Kaw sub-basin but of increasing importance as we move westward into the land of little rain. It is the factor of low and intermittent stream flows. Obviously very small populations can dangerously pollute a stream which, in dry periods, tends to disintegrate into a succession of stagnant pools or to disappear altogether.

Such streams are common *in the Republican River Sub-Basin*, particularly in the western portions. The bulk of the Kansas Basin Reservoir developments lies in this sub-basin. Of the 34 reservoirs originally planned for the basin as a whole in the so-called Pick-Sloan Plan (discussed in a later essay), 22, or two thirds of the total, lay on the Republican and its tributaries. Of the six reservoirs under construction in 1950, all but two lay in the Republican drainage area. These reservoirs constituted a major factor in the sub-basin's pollution-control problem.

This is thinly populated country; in an area of approximately 25,000 square miles live fewer than 80,000 people. Our investigators characterized the sources of pollution here as "only moderate." But they insisted that, however small quantitatively the amount of raw sewage and wastes dumped into the streams, the wastes create serious pollution problems. Why? Because the

streams have so little water in them, and because the amounts
fluctuate so widely. They fluctuate, too, in peculiar ways. Normally a river increases in volume as it flows downstream. How
could it do otherwise? It is being constantly fed by its tributaries
and by runoff water along its banks. Yet the Republican and its
branches do not, over major portions of their courses and during
critical periods, follow this seemingly inevitable pattern. Instead
they often have less water downstream than they do upstream.

The U. S. Geological Survey, in its *Water-Supply Paper* 273,
describes matters thus: "Throughout its course in Nebraska [the
Republican] flows in cretaceous deposits and is supplied by
spring-fed tributaries. In the western counties, where the rainfall
is small and the direct run-off rapid, the river is often dry, as for
example, in midsummer, immediately above mouths of Buffalo,
Rock, and Frenchman Creeks, but these streams revive the flow
of the river below their mouths. Such alternating dryness and
flow extend as far east as Superior, Nebraska, during droughts,
but only once in 12 years has the river ceased to flow at Red
Cloud and Superior."

What causes the river to deplete so drastically when, by ordinary standards, it ought to prosper? Evaporation is undoubtedly
a major factor. The Republican is, by and large, a wide and shallow river. A large percentage of its total volume lies exposed to
the dry hot winds and blazing suns of summer. Evaporation rates
approach 10 inches a month during July in the vicinity of the
Harlan County Dam, and such thieving raids upon a river already
shrunken might, by themselves, reduce its flow to nothing. Add to
this the water lost to narrow jungles of cottonwood and willow
along the banks and the water used in irrigation—for in the western reaches, the whole stream is sometimes diverted for irrigation
—add these losses, and the river's disappearance along stretches
between the mouths of spring-fed tributaries becomes plausible.

But our point is that such streams make mighty poor fluid

wastebaskets. Stinking Water Creek, one of them is called—and more than one deserve the name below outlets for untreated, or inadequately treated, sewage. Even downstream, where the river is larger, serious local pollutions were brought about by raw sewage disposals—for here the towns, generally speaking, are larger, too, and farmyards are closer together. Orleans, Alma, and Red Cloud in Nebraska, Concordia, Clay Center, and Junction City in Kansas—all pollute the stream with wholly untreated sewage.

The Orleans and Alma situations were given a special significance by the Harlan County Dam. The lake formed behind that dam, with its miles of shore line, was to be developed for recreational uses: swimming, boating, fishing, picnicking. Yet Orleans, only three miles or so above the upper end of that lake, discharged its sewage raw into the Republican—and that sewage included the wastes of what was reputed to be the largest cooperative creamery in the world. Though only 815 people are "connected" with sewers in Orleans, the pollution load has a population equivalent of 3,500—enough to make swimming a hazardous enterprise in the upper reaches of the lake. Concerning Alma, the situation was even more serious. The town lies directly on the shore, and its pollution load, dumped raw into the river, was equivalent to that of a population of 4,370.

Already mentioned have been the possible consequences of the Harlan County project on the mineral quality of the Kaw itself. Four pumping stations, two diversions, and an extensive canal system comprise the proposed irrigation developments below the big dam, and the river-bordering belt of irrigable lands extends all the way from Alma, Nebraska, to a few miles north of Concordia—a distance of 134 river miles. It is precisely here, at Concordia, that high salt concentrations are first introduced to the Republican. Buffalo Creek, which enters the Republican near Concordia, draws from salt springs and marshes in Jewell County,

Kansas, and from the salty Jamestown Marsh and the Little Marsh near Jamestown and Yuma, Kansas. Salt Creek, which discharges into the Republican several miles below Concordia, drains a salt marsh to the north. These discharges are, of course, reflected in the laboratory data on chloride concentrations. They do not, under present conditions of stream flow, constitute a particularly serious pollution problem, but if the upstream irrigation project drastically reduces flows below Concordia, even the Republican's waters may have a much lowered mineral quality. And when these waters mingle with those of the Smoky Hill at Junction City to form the Kaw, a truly serious downstream mineral pollution may be developed.

For saltiness is the pollution quality which chiefly distinguishes the *Smoky Hill Sub-Basin* from the other sub-basins of the Kansas. The Smoky Hill system has three main divisions: the drainage area of the Solomon, which branches off the main stream a few miles west of Abilene; the Saline, which branches off at Salina; and the Smoky Hill itself, which drains the southwestern portion of the entire basin. Each of these divides into numerous fingers probing the High Plains of western Kansas and eastern Colorado. As regards low and intermittent stream flows and the pollution problems arising therefrom, this sub-basin is not markedly different from the Republican. But as regards salinity, it is, in our basin, unique.

The problem, as might be expected, is concentrated in the drainage area of the Saline. Most of the 3,425 square miles of this area is underlain by a salt formation; were it completely excavated and spread evenly over the surface of Kansas, the entire state would be blanketed by a layer of solid sodium chloride 37 feet thick; and natural salt springs occur in the bed of the Saline and all its tributaries. To this natural pollution was added, in the 1920s and thereafter, the salt-brine disposals from oil and gas wells—for extensive fields of these lie within the Saline watershed.

As much as 400 barrels of salt brine may be pumped to obtain one barrel of oil in the Kansas fields, and one barrel of high-chloride oil brine may so contaminate 200 barrels of fresh water that it cannot be used for domestic purposes.

Popular pressure quickly dissuaded most oil companies from piping brine directly into streams, but their first alternative to this was but little better. It consisted of building ponds for holding the brine on the surface of the ground. Seeping down through soil and rock formations, the salt solutions polluted ground waters, which meant poisoned wells. It meant also, and eventually, poisoned streams—for streams are continuously fed by ground waters through springs. There is, indeed, no sharp distinction in nature between ground and surface waters; the two are continuous, minimum or basic stream flows being maintained during drought periods by ground waters.

Now of all forms of pollution, this is the most deadly in the literal meaning of the word. As it increases, it drastically modifies both the kind and amount of aquatic life in a stream. Moreover, salt dissolved in a river remains in solution all the way downstream, and the only way such pollution can be overcome is by dilution with fresh waters. Thus the Kansas State Board of Health found itself face to face with a pollution problem of emergency proportions, and it is to the credit of the Board's Sanitation Division and of the people of the state that the reaction to this emergency was both prompt and effective.

First, geologists and engineers worked out a method by which brine may be safely disposed of. Briefly, it consists of drilling wells to porous formations at depths well below the oil-bearing formation, and then dumping the brine into these. *Second,* a series of statutes pertaining to oil-field waters was enacted by the Kansas legislature—for candor compels the admission that, in cases like this, civic conscience cannot be depended upon to secure, unaided, the needed compliance: drilling deep wells costs money. *Third,* the legislation was tested in a series of suits brought by the oil companies or by the Board of Health and won, in every case, by the latter. In consequence Kansas by 1953 was well ahead of other states in its solution to this particular problem. Over $50,000,000 in new construction alone had been spent by oil companies on this program; since that program's inception, not a single city has had to abandon a source of water supply because of brine. Moreover, civic virtue—even a coerced civic virtue—had proved to be individually profitable. Wherever this disposal method is used, oil production has been unexpectedly yet significantly increased.

But as we've pointed out, natural salt pollution remained a problem whose possible enhancement, by a reduction in Republican stream flows, was cause for grave concern, determining a special attention to chloride concentrations by our basin investigators.

3

The Sickness of the River and the Health of Man   It is necessary to keep the river's disease, which is highly infectious, from spreading to man. The waters we have fouled must be cleansed before we partake of them. For this we spend millions.

Approximately 35,000,000 people in the United States, and more than half our industries, depend upon filtered surface-water supplies—water drawn from streams and reservoirs. About 1,500,-000,000,000 (that's 1,500 billion!) gallons are treated and filtered annually in this country at a cost estimated several years ago at $150,000,000, and the cost goes up as pollution increases.

In the Kansas Basin, five municipalities draw all or substantial portions of their water from rivers. These communities spend tens of thousands of dollars annually to maintain and operate water-treatment plants. Even so, they do not spend enough. In 1946, the

Kansas State Board of Health, in co-operation with the U. S. Public Health Service, made a study of public water-supply facilities in Kansas as a whole and found that $21,200,000 worth of improvements were needed to safeguard public health. A considerable portion of this total was assigned to communities drawing on rivers in the Kaw system. There has been some improvement since 1946, but in 1952, 17 per cent of all the public water supplies in Kansas still did not meet the Drinking Water Standards of the Public Health Service.

We've indicated in our preceding section how a substantial part of water-treatment expense must go toward removing the pollution caused by excessive raw sewage disposals upstream. Marysville, Kansas, for example, finds its water problems complicated and its treatment costs increased by raw sewage dumped into the Big Blue by Beatrice, Nebraska, a city of 13,000 some 50 miles upstream. We've mentioned Lawrence, Kansas. It spends considerably more on water treatment each year than it would have to spend were not the Kaw dangerously polluted 35 miles upstream by Topeka, a city of more than 80,000 with extensive manufactories and large packing plants. Topeka does have a sewage-treatment plant, but it is inadequate. Only about a third of the city's sewage is treated there when the plant is running, and when it is shut down—as it often is during times of high water, in order to clean the tanks (and this at the precise time when pollution is most serious!)—all Topeka's sewage goes raw into the river.

The process of treatment at Lawrence is typical. This city of 18,000 draws two thirds of its water from the Kaw, the other third from wells, treating it in a plant built in 1916. First the water is partially sterilized with chlorine; pre-chlorination, this is called, because it takes place prior to the main treatment. Then the water is treated with alum, iron, and lime for flocculation, alum (as aluminum sulphate) reacting with lime to form aluminum hydroxide, iron sulphate reacting with lime to form iron hydroxide. The flocculent thus produced sweeps like an extremely fine-toothed comb through the water, cleaning out suspended materials. The water then pours (looking like smoke, with flocculent) into settling basins, where solids settle out, after which it flows through a succession of filters. These are layers of sand of a specified size, 36 inches thick. The water is then "softened" by treatment with lime and soda ash—which takes out such substances as calcium, magnesium, iron, and manganese—after which bicarbonate (having an acid reaction) is used to reduce the softener-induced alkalinity. The water is finally chlorinated again (*post*-chlorination) and pumped into the pipes of the Lawrence water system. Every other day each filter is cleaned by a process called "backwashing." The filter tank is emptied, water is forced through the sand from the bottom, and the accumulated filth of forty-eight hours boils up in liquid clouds to be flushed away by powerful streams of clean water.

In this way the Lawrence plant treats some 3,000,000 gallons of water daily, or about 2,000 gallons per minute. The annual cost of operation, including plant repairs and replacements, wages for employees, and treating materials, amounts to $5.24 per capita, and to this must be added amortization costs of the original plant investment. In smaller communities the per capita costs of safe water go up. Building a waterworks may cost only 1 to 8 per cent of the annual spendable incomes of citizens in the larger towns of the basin as compared to 25 or 35 per cent for those living in towns of a few hundred. It is in consequence of this that health problems arising from unsanitary water are most serious in these little towns. . . .

Nor is the use of water for domestic purposes the only way in which the river's disease may be communicated to man. Swimmers almost invariably swallow some of the water in which they swim, and many a case of typhoid has been attributed to swimming in polluted streams. Hence the concern over the Orleans and Alma, Nebraska, sewage disposal in waters which, as part of the Harlan County reservoir development, will be used for recreation. Still more serious is the public health threat posed by use of polluted waters for irrigation. A death-breeding short cut from anus to mouth is all too efficiently achieved if low-growing fruits and vegetables are irrigated with raw sewage and then consumed by men. Even field crops such as corn may become contaminated if irrigated with diseased waters. In general, water diverted from the river channel for irrigation purposes is removed from areas of limited access and spread over areas where many men and their livestock may make contact with it. It is therefore especially important that a river so used be healthy.

We've said that when a scientist investigates an object he traces out a pattern of possible action upon it. Essentially the process of investigation *is* a programming of action. Certainly that is true in the present case. As our investigators made a precise definition of the pollution problem in the Kansas Basin they developed a detailed outline of the problem's solution, and in so far as the definition was confined to technical matters the solution is similarly limited. (The fact that the river is a social as well as a technical problem complicates things, as we've seen.) Technically speaking, then, we know what to do—and what *not* to do—to solve the Kansas Basin pollution problem.

So far as sewage pollution is concerned, we may sum up both the positive and the negative in a maxim: *no sewage whatever should be dumped raw into a stream: ALL should be treated before being disposed of in rivers.* The degree of needed treatment varies, however, with the amount and kind of sewage and the quantity and quality of water in the river. Sometimes "primary" treatment is sufficient, taken in conjunction with the stream's natural digestive capacities. Sometimes "secondary" treatment is also necessary.

But what constitutes "primary" treatment? It is as simple as can be. Merely running the sewage water through a fine screen will reduce the amount of suspended solids by 20 to 25 per cent, the number of bacteria by 10 to 20 per cent, and the amount of oxygen required for digestion by 5 or 10 per cent. If to screening is added a sedimentation process, whereby the sewage water is held in settling basins for a specified length of time, from 40 to 70 per cent of the suspended solids is removed, the bacterial count is reduced anywhere from 25 to 75 per cent, and the oxygen demand is cut by 25 to 40 per cent. These two processes of screening and sedimentation constitute "primary" treatment, and, we repeat, *no* sewage whatever should be dumped into the river without having had at least this much reduction.

Of "secondary" treatments—and some such treatment is absolutely needed where the proportion of sewage to river volume is high—there are two main kinds.

The more complex of the two is the "activated-sludge" process, whereby partially digested sewage solids, properly "activated" with bacteria, are used to speed the digestion of new, raw sewage. The two thirds or less of Topeka's sewage which is treated at all goes through an activated-sludge plant. Here the basic operations are three: First, the sewage, after passing through screens and settling tanks, is mixed with from 20 to 35 per cent of its volume of biologically active sludge. Second, the mixture is agitated with air, which is forced through it and in the presence of which the bacterial digesters multiply rapidly; organic solids are swiftly oxidized and suspended materials tend to coagulate in forms which are easily settleable. Third, this final settlement takes place in special tanks. The water which flows out at the end of this process—the "effluent," as it is called—is clear and sparkling and contains very little organic material.

The other main secondary treatment is the "trickling filter" process, so named because its principal element is the trickling of sewage water over and through a 6- to 8-foot-deep bed of broken stones, each of which is 2 to 4 inches thick. A great advantage of this process, and one which recommends it highly to small communities, is its simplicity. No considerable technical knowledge is required for its comprehension, and its operation requires little skill. The process, indeed, is virtually automatic.

Take the Smith Center, Kansas, plant for example—built in the late 1940s after decades in which the town's filth piled up in a stinking, fly-breeding mess below the sewage outlet. The sewage water now enters the plant through a screen which separates out the coarser solids, flowing thence into a settling basin called an Imhoff tank after the German, Karl Imhoff, who invented it. This tank is designed in such a way that gas bubbles from digesting solids at its bottom will not agitate the raw sewage above sufficiently to interfere with further settling. The tank stands several feet above the circular filtering bed. This enables a siphon arrangement at the exit trough to operate a rotary distributor turning above the bed. Through it, the sewage water (which has now had primary treatment) is sprayed over the coarse stones. From the filter bottom, through an underdrain system, the sewage water goes into the final settling tank, from which the sludge—a black tarlike substance—is obtained. This sludge may then be thrown back into the Imhoff tank for digestion or it may be put into a special digestion tank. Again, the effluent is clear, sparkling water containing very small amounts of organic material.

Activated-sludge plants, properly operated, will reduce the oxygen demand by 85 to 95 per cent, the suspended solids in the same proportion, and will remove from 90 to 98 per cent of all bacteria. Trickling filter plants are only slightly less effective. They'll reduce oxygen demand by 80 to 95 per cent, suspended solids by 70 to 92 per cent, and bacteria by 90 to 95 per cent.

But the prevention of pollution is not the sole value which may be obtained from these treatment processes. The fermentation of sludge in a digestion tank yields a highly combustible gas which may be piped away and used to operate plant machinery. The gas produced at the Topeka plant is so used, and in some cities considerable areas are lighted with electricity produced by generators whose only fuel is sewer gas. Important portions of plant operating costs may be so recovered. And further recoveries may be made if, with our science, we follow the good advice of Victor Hugo in *Les Miserables* and return to the soil some of the wealth we have taken from it. Doing so enables us to reverse what is now a pernicious process, for instead of spreading disease we improve health.

The sewage sludge which is left after complete digestion comprises a humus immensely rich in plant food, and sludge is even richer in nitrates if digestion is not carried to its ultimate end— as it need not be. There exists in all the world no better substance for revivifying an exhausted soil, and it is a clean substance which, unlike barnyard manure, may be pleasantly as well as safely handled. Phosphorus and potassium, in addition to nitrogen, are found here in proportions that compare favorably with most manufactured fertilizers, and in forms more readily assimilable by living plants. Also found are elements which, though needed by the plant in very small quantities, are nonetheless essential to its healthy growth—such elements as sulphur, iron, manganese, magnesium, boron, copper, and zinc. These are generally not found at all in the fertilizer one buys.

At present, in recklessly extravagant America, most of this wealth is thrown away. At Smith Center, Kansas, for example, great piles of it stand below the final settling basin, seemingly undiscovered by enterprising farmers or gardeners. But there are a few cities which pay substantial portions of their sewage-treatment costs by marketing the treatment's end product. "Milorganite" is the trade name for the fertilizer (fortified sewage sludge) produced by Milwaukee, and "Soiltone" is the trade name for the dry, pulverized, digested sludge obtained from the Lincoln and Des Moines plants. It is to be hoped that the example provided by these cities will be increasingly imitated. . . .

Thus we possess techniques for preventing, absolutely, the pollution of streams through sewage disposal in them. We have only to respect with our science the living integrity of the river, never assigning to its waters a greater organic waste than those waters can safely consume. We possess, too, in a red-backed report of the basin investigation, specific recommendations for the application of these techniques to the Kansas system. There remains the necessity for carrying out these recommendations, a process requiring social action.

4

There Ought to Be a Law!   In Kansas the action was promptly initiated, as those who know the state well would expect it to be.

If Kansas has not recently been notably progressive in other fields of social legislation, she has always been so in the field of public health. Perhaps, as has been hinted,[1] this can be explained by the Puritan tradition in which the state was founded and to which she yet, in several respects, adheres, for Kansans seem to believe that the purity of one's spirit can shine only through a body well scrubbed and healthy. Whatever the reason, Kansas organized her State Board of Health in 1885, has consistently given it a greater authority and a firmer financial support than most such boards receive, and through it has pioneered many a valuable health movement. The famed "Swat the Fly" campaign which swept the nation in the early 1900s was initiated by the then State Health Officer of Kansas, Dr. S. J. Crumbine. In 1907 a model stream-pollution-control act was passed by the Kansas

[1]See the second essay, page 53.

legislature, requiring each city or industry to obtain a permit from the Health Board before running wastes into a stream. In 1909 Kansas outlawed the common drinking cup—the first state to do so. It was a Kansas schoolteacher, Frank Rose, who invented the fly swatter in 1906, and a few years later another Kansan, Hugh Moore, invented the sanitary paper drinking cup and the penny-cup vending machine to dispense it.

Thus the Kansas Board's Sanitation Division (established in 1907, when the basic water-pollution act was passed) followed distinguished precedent when it worked out a proposed policy for pollution abatement a few months after the basin investigation was completed. Public hearings on the proposed policy were held in all major communities affected by it, and in consequence of the overwhelmingly favorable response to it, the policy was adopted. It listed six precise goals and issued time schedules for initiation and completion, by cities and industries, of the treatment measures through which the goals can be achieved. This schedule can be enforced by the Board of Health's control over sewage permits, provided for by the basic 1907 law: discharge of sewage into a stream without a permit is punishable by heavy fines.

The other two states involved in the investigation had not, when this was written, responded to the recommendations of the survey as effectively as Kansas had done. In large part this is due to deficiencies in enabling legislation, both in Nebraska and Colorado, and to inadequate provisions for staff. Neither state had comprehensive water-pollution-control legislation of the kind Kansas has had since 1907.

There was one respect, however, in which Nebraska's statutes dealing with pollution control were definitely superior to those of Kansas.

In Nebraska all villages and cities may issue what are called "mortgage bonds" which do not impose any general liability upon the municipality but are specifically secured by the property for which the money is borrowed. Thus bonds issued to build a sewage plant and a sewer system could be secured by the plant and the sewers and paid off by the revenues from these. This definitely implies that those people and industries who are serviced by the sewer system and plant may be charged for that service, a provision which is of great help to the financing of sewage-treatment works by municipalities. It makes possible the fair distribution of operating-cost payments among those who benefit from them: those who receive more pay more in service charges; those who receive less pay less—the same principle which is employed in the financing of public water supplies or municipally owned electricity. The arrangement seems obviously equitable and easily made.

In Kansas, however, it was not permitted by law in first- and second-class cities. Since 1929 third-class cities had been allowed to make sewer service charges if they wished, and Ellsworth, Kansas, promptly took advantage of this permission when she purchased a private sewer system. Other third-class towns followed suit. Cities of larger population, however, were denied this authority, and this meant that some of them were unable to raise more than one fourth of the operating costs of their existing sewage-treatment plants. When plant enlargements were needed the situation was even worse. The consequence was, on occasion, a serious and (under existing legislation) virtually insoluble pollution problem.

Take the case of Fort Scott, Kansas. It lies outside the Kansas Basin, but its experience is illustrative of the general problem. When this was written, Fort Scott was discharging untreated sewage into the Marmaton River, and since the early 1930s the Board of Health had received a steady stream of petitions and complaints from property owners downstream. In October 1945 the Board ordered Fort Scott to treat its sewage and cease the pollution of the stream. A year later, the order having been ignored, action was initiated in the district court to compel compliance. The city then prepared plans for a plant which would give primary treatment of the sewage, but it also proved that it could, under the present tax laws, raise only 40 per cent of the proposed plant's operating costs. The court case was still pending when this was written, postponed in the hope that some equitable arrangement could be worked out.

A few years ago the Board of Health selected at random 22 first- and second-class Kansas cities and studied their financing of sewage treatment. It was found that 20 of the 22 could not, under existing legislation, obtain enough revenue to operate their plants. Only 20 per cent of the needed money could be raised in some cities.

Obviously the only answer was passage of the needed permissive legislation. Why, then, was this not done?

Certainly it was not for lack of trying. Again and again the needed bill was introduced in the Kansas legislature, buttressed by expert testimony and supported by sportsmen's organizations and other popular groups. Again and again the bill died in committee or was killed on the floor. The manner of its death signifies once more that the problem of the river is, in the last analysis, a problem of men, and that a quality of moral corruption in the body politic may sometimes be gauged by the quantity of physical pollution in a stream.

"Corruption" is certainly too strong a description of the present case. But the fact remains that this repeated rejection of needed legislation did not proceed from the popular will. Rather it proceeded largely from the special interests of packing plants, and particularly from a large company in Topeka. To see how great this special interest was, and how inequitable was the system of financing sewage disposal, we can compare this company with the Santa Fe Railroad company. Under prevailing laws, sewage disposal was paid for out of property taxes—and on this basis Santa Fe, which maintains large offices and shops in Topeka, paid some $4,000 annually toward collection and treatment of the city's sewage. The packing company, on the other hand, paid only $400 in such taxes. Yet Santa Fe contributed very little sewage beyond that of the population it employs, whereas the packing company discharged wastes costing the city some $40,000 a year to handle and treat. In other words, the packing company paid just 1 per cent of the cost of handling the wastes it discharged, and its privately profitable business was in effect subsidized by other taxpayers to the tune of over $3,000 a month.

If these facts had been widely publicized, and if the packing company had appeared openly in the fight against sewer-charge legislation, the latter would undoubtedly have been on Kansas books long ago. (Similar laws were in effect in 28 states and worked well.) But those who stand to gain from inequitable arrangements generally prefer subterfuge and indirection to a frank and open battle, and they are aided in this by a press which feels small responsibility for actively uncovering and developing the news. The packers never openly showed their hand; they enlisted the support of the Kansas Chamber of Commerce, most of whose members had little or no conception of the issue; and the general impression was created that the proposed legislation was mandatory rather than permissive in character and that it was "just another bill to increase taxes." Thus defeat was assured.

What happened in 1949 was typical. The State Board of Health, having been urged to do so by several cities, joined in the drafting of the needed bill. In the drafting conferences, as a matter of fact, 24 municipalities and one township participated. The bill was presented to the House Committee on Hygiene and Public Health, which held two hearings upon it and heard testimony unanimously favorable to it. The measure was then passed out as a committee bill and given House Number 224. But at this point word came down from the Executive Mansion. The governor was persuaded that the bill violated his campaign promise of "no tax increases" (though in fact it did not), and he therefore hoped it would not come to a floor vote. Why not, as quietly as possible, bury it alive?

A convenient device exists for just that purpose in the Kansas legislature, as it does in most legislative bodies. There is a State Affairs Committee whose members are well aware that bills referred to them are, generally speaking, to be acted upon unfavorably: they refer to themselves jocularly as the "graveyard committee." And when—abruptly and with no public explanation —House Bill Number 224 was sent to them they did their jobs well. Despite the fact that the committee competent to pass on such legislation had held full hearings and, on the basis of them, approved the measure, the State Affairs Committee held a hearing of its own. Just one hearing. Though it was by no means widely publicized in advance, at least 25 people came to argue for the bill while only two came to oppose it. The bill was then disapproved. . . .

5

Silt Pollution: A Wider Reference   We have left to the last a brief consideration of the problem of silt pollution and its abatement. We have done so, not because it is of minor importance— indeed turbidity produced by erosion silt is, as we've seen, integral to the problem of organic pollution—but because a consideration of it leads us inevitably to that wider reference whose nature, or an understanding of it, is the over-all aim of our thinking about a river.

In addition to the turbidity it produces in the body of a stream, erosion silt affects water use and river development in two important ways. It complicates the processes by which water is purified for drinking purposes, and it increases the costs and lowers the long-time effectiveness of dams and reservoirs.

A decade ago the Soil Conservation Service made a study of water treatment in 22 cities of the Piedmont area in North Carolina. It was found that the average treatment cost there, including overhead and amortization of plant and equipment, was $70 per million gallons (it must certainly be much higher today), of which $27 was for treatment processes and $5 for chemicals—the chief of the latter being alum, used for the settlement of suspended solids.

The Service estimated that an adequate soil-conservation program in that region would reduce the suspended load of streams by 30 per cent at least—and this would result in an average *immediate* saving of $1.50 per million gallons. "Considering the future savings from smaller capital outlay for new settling basins and plant equipment, reduced flushing costs and other plant operations, the total savings eventually would be $7 per million gallons or $94,000 annually for the 22 cities. If we could save only $1 per million gallons on all of the surface water of the United States which had to be filtered for domestic or industrial use, we would bring about an annual benefit of $1,400,000. We should be able to save at least seven times this much, or around $10,000,000 annually, to municipalities and industries through soil conservation work on the watershed above the reservoirs."[1]

More serious by far is the reduction of reservoir capacity by sedimentation. It has been estimated[2] that the annual cost of

[1]*Stream Pollution by Erosion Silt*, H. H. Bennett, Chief, Soil Conservation Service. Reprinted from hearings before the Committee on Rivers and Harbors on water-pollution-control bills Nos. 13, 14, 15, and 20, 1945.

[2]By H. H. Bennett in Foreword to *The Control of Reservoir Silting*, by Carl B. Brown, U. S. Department of Agriculture, Miscellaneous Publication No. 521.

reservoir silting a decade ago was upward of $50,000,000 and that many reservoirs important to our war effort in 1944 were losing 1, 2, 3, and even 5 per cent of their capacity every year through silting.

Because of soil erosion, an important factor to be considered in the design of reservoirs is the so-called "capacity-watershed ratio." If two reservoirs of the same size are located in areas having the same erosion rate, the reservoir which drains the larger area will, of course, silt up more rapidly than that which drains the smaller one. The capacity-watershed (C/W) ratio is a figure indicating the relationship of reservoir capacity to watershed area, the former being stated in acre-feet, the latter in square miles, and some very costly errors in design have stemmed from a failure to give this ratio its proper weight. One of them occurred only a few years ago at Osborne, Kansas, on the Solomon River. Here a water-supply reservoir was built in 1936 at a cost of approximately $150,000—a very substantial cost for a municipality of some 1,900 population. *Within one year* after completion, that reservoir was completely filled with silt! At least a dozen similar failures of reservoirs constructed since 1930 are on record. Some of the most spectacular dams in the West—which is to say in the world—now have their usefulness reduced at an alarming rate by siltation. Erosion debris is piling up at a much greater rate than anticipated in Lake Mead, the reservoir formed by the giant Hoover Dam. The same thing is happening to the reservoir behind the Elephant Butte Dam.

But it must be emphasized that the importance of the C/W ratio depends upon the rate of erosion, and its value as a determinant of reservoir design can be greatly varied by the establishment of soil-conservation practices. Indeed, the purely technical possibilities of watershed-erosion control are very great. Merely by assigning each acre to the uses for which it is best fitted—protecting highly erosible slopes with permanent vegetative cover and practicing good rotations on all cultivated land—soil losses can be cut to a fraction of their former amount on most watersheds, and surface-water runoff, so important to flood-control planning, can be significantly reduced. Consider, for example, research data obtained at Bethany, Missouri, on Shelby Silt Loam, a soil type similar to those covering large parts of the Kansas River Basin. The land on which the experiments were made had a slope of 8 per cent, which is to say that it had an 8-foot vertical drop for every 100 feet on the horizonal. When planted continuously to corn, it lost nearly 19 tons of soil per acre each year over a 10-year period. When planted to a recommended rotation of corn, barley, and clover-timothy, it lost only a little more than 4 tons per acre annually, a reduction of almost 80 per cent in soil-loss rates. Water losses, too, were reduced, though not so drastically. Land cropped continuously in corn lost, as surface runoff, a little more than 27 per cent of all the rain falling upon it, whereas the land in 3-year rotation lost only a little more than 16 per cent.

When to these general use assignments are added other soil-saving devices—such as contour tillage, strip cropping, terracing, and gully-control dams—runoff and soil-loss rates are still further cut. Straight-row up-and-down cultivation was compared with contour cultivation (in which the rows run level around the slopes) on land with a slope of between 6 and 7 per cent at the Bethany experiment station. All other factors influencing erosion and runoff rates were held constant. It was found that land cultivated in a straight row lost nearly 164 tons of soil per acre while land cultivated on the contour lost only 21.31 tons per acre over a 7-year period. Sixteen per cent of the water falling on the straight-rowed field was lost as runoff, while 14 per cent of the water falling on the contoured field was so lost. Strip cropping, in which alternating strips of row and cover crops are planted on the contour, thus breaking up a long slope into a series of shorter ones, markedly increases the effectiveness of contour cultivation. If terracing is combined with strip cropping, a still greater reduction of soil and water losses may be effected.

Small wonder that many cities now are actively concerning themselves with the promotion of soil-conserving practices in the watersheds feeding their reservoirs. The experience of Decatur, Illinois, is representative. This city draws its water from the artificial Lake Decatur, backed up by a dam which (with the needed land) cost $2,013,000. In 1936 a survey revealed that in 14 years the reservoir had lost more than 14 per cent of its original capacity of nearly 20,000 acre-feet. The city fathers were justifiably alarmed, and their alarm was compounded when industrial users of water began making plans to move elsewhere: one of the city's largest soybean-processing plants, for example, took an option on an alternative factory site on Lake Erie. So in 1941 the city began appropriating $12,000 a year to promote erosion control in the lake's 906-square-mile watershed; two full-time soil-conservation specialists were hired, and a 10-year program designed to provide complete conservation practices on a majority of the watershed farms was inaugurated.

Our main point, however, is that this kind of water-pollution problem requires for its solution a much wider frame of reference than does the problem of sewage disposal—assuming for the moment that the latter can be treated in isolation. Abatement of pollution by municipalities and private industries requires, as we have seen, social action—but it is action confined for the most part to the stream itself and its banks. Not so the abatement of erosion-silt pollution. This problem can be solved only in terms of the watershed as a whole, and it requires the co-operation not only of highly organized groups—like city governments and industries—but of farmers who, despite the Federal farm programs (indeed, largely because of them), yet remain unorganized, largely self-determining entrepreneurs. Town and country must work together.

In this connection, the stated objectives of the conservation association formed in Decatur, Illinois, are significant. One of them is "to foster rural-urban co-operation in an attack on soil wastage." The statement continues: "Since the loss in soil results in lower soil productivity and purchasing power, lowered land values, reservoir and stream silting, and decreased standards of living, all of which affect both farm and city people, it is important that the attack be united."

A recognition of the necessity for thinking in terms of this wider reference, the watershed as a whole, when planning pollution-abatement programs is indicated by Public Law 845, adopted in 1948 by the 80th Congress. This was an act "to provide for water pollution control activities." Section 1 declared it to be the policy of the Congress to "recognize, preserve, and protect the primary responsibilities and rights of the states in controlling water pollution" but to help the states carry out their responsibilities by providing them with technical assistance and financial aid. Section 2 ordered the Surgeon General (chief of the Public Health Service), "after careful investigation, and in co-operation with other Federal agencies, with State water pollution agencies and interstate agencies, and with municipalities and industries involved, [to] prepare or adopt comprehensive programs for eliminating or reducing the pollution of interstate waters and tributaries thereof and improving the sanitary condition of surface and underground waters." The key words here were *co-operation* and *comprehensive*. The latter was significantly repeated in the next sentence of the act: "In the development of such comprehensive programs due regard shall be given to the improvements which are necessary to conserve such waters for public water supplies, propagation of fish and aquatic life, recreational purposes, and agricultural, industrial, and other legitimate uses."

What did this mean? Clearly implied was an integrated

multiple-use approach to basin planning. The Congress wanted public health to have its proper place in such planning and specifically ordered Federal sanitation officers to regard their work as part of a whole development program. It was an indispensable part, but *only* a part. It must be performed in harmony with other elements of the total program.

And there was solid basis for hope in the fact that even those technicians whose highly specialized concern was with sewage treatment were realizing that their specialty could not be successfully dealt with in isolation from other watershed concerns. Wrote Karl Imhoff and Gordon Fair in their authoritative book, *Sewage Treatment:*[3]

Sewage treatment is but one of many factors in a true and full economy of water. This should be appreciated by all who are concerned with the disposal of sewage and industrial wastes but particularly by central river authorities. . . . The engineer charged with the design of a sewage-treatment plant can best meet his responsibility to the individual community that he serves by taking a broad view of the *regional* problems involved.

[3]New York: John Wiley and Sons, Inc., 1940. Page 2.

The Evolution of River Planning

V

1

Of Flood Control and Navigation   In the preceding essay we focused on that *particular* aspect of the river with which we as "watery beings" are most intimately involved. We began by considering the river in its seemingly contradictory roles of sewer and source of drinking water; but as we proceeded we found that the seeming contradiction need not be one at all. If we treat the river, through our science, with a decent respect for its flowing integrity, the "contradiction" reveals itself as but another instance of paradox—and paradox is of the nature of all ultimate truths in our world of continuous change. Though we con-

centrated at first on the body of the river itself, including its
banks, we soon found that this was not enough. The more sharply
we analyzed and the more deeply we probed this problem
of pollution abatement, the more we found the "particular" becoming the "general." We found that, to deal successfully with
this particular problem, we had to involve larger and larger areas
of land along the river's banks until at last our concern was with
the whole watershed; and we found that a statement of the
problem in exclusively physical, technical terms was inadequate
to a final solution of it. The final solution involves a translation
of physical science into social philosophy, for as the social
significance of river-pollution abatement widens from municipality to state and finally to Federal government we are forced to
consider it as but one aspect of a total regional development plan.

In this present essay let us focus at the outset on another
particular aspect of the river—and let us begin with the Wild
Missouri, whose lower reaches are swollen by the waters and
clogged by the erosion debris of the Kansas Basin.

There was a note of ominous prophecy in the very manner in
which the Missouri was discovered. Marquette and Joliet did
it by ear. They heard the river before they saw it—and both sight
and sound were terrible.

On that June day of 1673 the two French Jesuits were already,
as we've observed, in an apprehensive mood. The sight of those
huge painted gods on the rock cliff above the river, paintings
savagely conceived and brutally executed, had strangely dis-
turbed their piety. When a vast roaring sound reached their ears,
growing steadily louder as they moved downstream, they began
to proceed very cautiously indeed. They believed they were ap-
proaching a rapid, or perhaps a waterfall, and they probably
paddled their canoes close to the riverbank. Indications are that
this bank was on what is now the Missouri side of the Mississippi,

for they were nearly swamped when they moved suddenly abreast the mouth of a river unlike any they, or perhaps any other European, had ever seen. The sight confirmed the terror of the sound.

Wrote Marquette: "An accumulation of large, entire trees, branches, and floating islands was issuing from the mouth . . . with such impetuosity that we could not, without great danger, risk passing through it." But pass through it they did, narrowly escaping death—and the Mississippi they traveled was no longer a river immense but clean. It was all stained with mud, threatful with driftwood. . . .

The story of the Missouri thus begins with a "June rise." It was more severe than most, judging from the account, but no more severe than has occurred many times since settlement began. Undoubtedly this first recorded flood was formed by a coincidence of two towering crests, one piled on top of the other. The first of these was shaped in the river's upper system where melting ice and snow, pouring down the mountains and off the plains, had swollen all the streams. Inexorably this crest flowed southeast to encounter crests which had flowed almost due east, having been shaped by heavy rains in the areas drained by the Missouri's lower system, including particularly the Kansas River Basin. The two floods together poured out over flood plains where today lie cities and scores of towns and a great wealth of farms.

Nearly all of the more disastrous floods on the lower Missouri have been so formed, and the list of them is long and depressing.

The first of which height records were kept has already been mentioned: the tremendous flood of 1844. It caused relatively little damage measurable in monetary terms, for most of the country it overran was wilderness, and the remainder was sparsely settled. But were a flood of similar proportions to occur today, its damage would amount to hundreds of millions of dollars for Kansas City alone, exceeding even the damage caused in 1951. Prior to '51, the most disastrous flood for Kansas City was that of 1903, caused by a high crest on the Kaw running head on into a Missouri already out of its banks. The latter was abruptly raised some 14 feet above flood stage. Stockyards, railroad freight yards, packing plants, mills—the whole industrial center built on the wedge of flat lowland bounded by the two rivers—lay under deep and turbulent waters. Eight thousand freight cars were submerged, and 23,000 people were homeless.

But this, the most famous of the Missouri floods until '51, was little if any more disastrous than several others. In 1881, 1903, 1908, 1909, 1915, 1927, 1935, 1942, 1943, 1944, 1945, and 1947—in 12 years out of 66—high floods occurred. Those of 1942, 1943, and 1944—the most destructive three-year period in the river's history until '51—caused damage estimated at more than $150,000,000 through the great valley as a whole. The 1943 flood covered 2,260,000 acres and ruined some $40,000,000 worth of farm crops; it did an estimated $65,000,000 of damage altogether. The 1947 flood caused an estimated $111,000,000 of damage.

Within the Kansas Basin, the two largest cities, Kansas City, Kansas, and Topeka, the Kansas capital, contained valuable property concentrated in areas vulnerable to floods from the Kaw, and they sustained the greatest damages when the great floods came. They are not, however, the only basin cities seriously threatened, as we saw in our opening essay. Floods are frequent at Manhattan, a city of 17,000 at the junction of the Kaw and Blue; at Junction City, with 11,000, where the Republican and Smoky Hill come together; at Salina, with 25,000, on the Smoky Hill; and in a dozen communities along the middle and lower portions of the Republican. To the Republican, indeed, goes the cruel distinction of having killed more people at one swoop than any other stream in the Kansas system. One hundred people drowned along the Republican in 1935 when a wholly unheralded 15-foot wall of water came roaring down the channel, submerging great acreages of farmland in a few minutes and destroying $9,000,000 of property. On June 22, 1947, thirteen people lost their lives in Cambridge, Nebraska, when the Republican went on another rampage.

Small wonder that the loudest demand for Missouri River development was essentially a negative one, made chiefly by cities. Stop this repeated flooding of urban areas! Keep the river away from our doors! Do whatever is necessary upstream to protect the wealth concentrated downstream! Kansas City, the most vulnerable to floods of all the valley's larger towns, was the most insistent in these demands, but other downstream towns joined in right heartily.

These appeals were of course made to the Congress, who, through appropriate legislation, assigned the task of answering them in action to the Corps of Engineers, United States Army (we will consider later how the Army Engineers became "Engineers to the Congress," and whether this arrangement is good or bad for our democracy). Hence one of the first great river engineering efforts undertaken by the Engineers was devoted not to harnessing the river's energies but to walling them away from areas where, unloosed, they wreaked the greatest havoc. This meant building levees. Some $55,000,000 had been spent up to 1945 on levees in the Missouri system, and while they did some good the final results were far less than satisfactory. For one thing, the Missouri and its tributaries carry enormous amounts of silt and sediment; 100,000,000 tons of silt were poured by the Missouri into the Mississippi each year on the average, and deposits of these kept raising the river beds. Flood control then required an equivalent raising of levee heights—and each increase in height meant greater risk of structural failure. Furthermore, the levees prevented the river's normal horizontal expansion in time of high flow, and this meant, of course, an increased vertical expansion. "The confinement of flood flows by levees has substantially raised flood heights," reported General Edgar C. Jadwin,[1] then Chief of the U. S. Army Corps of Engineers, after the tragic 1927 flood on the Missouri and lower Mississippi. And the 1927 disaster destroyed popular as well as technical faith in levees as (by themselves) controllers of floods.

The effectiveness of levees could be increased somewhat by channel straightening, and a good deal of this was done by Army Engineers. More was contemplated. By ironing out some of the channel kinks, engineers enabled the river to discharge more rapidly its burden of water, thus reducing the chances of a piling up of flood crests where tributaries join the main stem. But a truly adequate control seemed obviously to require, among other things, a group of mutually sustaining reservoirs. Dams were needed behind which surplus water could be piled up until such time as river channels could safely carry it. And to the construction of these the Engineers now turned. Flood control gave way to flood prevention, in long-time river plans.

The first big flood-control reservoir was formed by the Fort Peck Dam across the Missouri in Montana. Completed in 1939 at a cost of $130,000,000, it has been called the largest earth-fill dam in the world. It is four miles long, close to a mile wide at its base, and rises to a maximum height of 250 feet above the river bed. The lake forming behind it is the second largest reservoir in the world, spreading across 245,000 acres and having a 1,600-mile shore line. But a glance at the map will reveal that this reservoir, vast as it is, is relatively a mere speck on the surface of the valley, and it lies far northwest of the portions of the valley, the North Platte and Kansas basins, which have the heaviest rainfall and produce more than half of the downstream floods. Much, much more was needed—and much, much more was planned for.

[1]Quoted by Rufus Terral in his *The Missouri Valley*. New Haven: Yale University Press, 1947.

But dam and levee building was not sparked by flood-control needs alone. Another major motive was the desire to maintain or create a navigable channel from Sioux City down 815 miles to the Missouri's mouth—and this in turn had as motive an issue which, at a first ignorant glance, might seem little related to river-channel development. This issue was the freight-rate structure of the railroads.

Only apparently do we digress from our main subject when we explain that, historically, no single factor was more important in determining an almost exclusively agrarian economy over most of the vast valley than an incredibly complex and obviously unfair system of railroad rates. Through it the Middle West was made an economic vassal of the industrialized East and West coasts. It was actually cheaper in many instances to ship raw materials to the East or West, process them there, and ship them back into the valley as finished goods than it was to process them where they were produced and ship the goods elsewhere.

For instance, it would seem inevitable that Omaha would be the center of livestock slaughtering and packing for Iowa and Nebraska, that nearly all the animals produced in the area immediately adjacent to Omaha would be shipped to this city's packing plants. All the "laws" of economics would seem to dictate the shipment of live animals only a few miles (between 300 and 400 at most) in preference to shipping them a thousand, then processing them at the end of these few miles, and finally shipping the meat (which is certainly cheaper to handle than livestock) to such hugely consuming areas as, say, Los Angeles. But such "laws" mean nothing in the weird economic world created by the rate makers. From Omaha it was cheaper to ship live animals than dressed meat. Much cheaper.

"A 200-pound live hog can be shipped from Omaha to Los Angeles for $2," explained Rufus Terral in his *The Missouri*

Valley, published in 1947,[2] "but to ship 150 pounds of pork from the same hog costs $3.75. Nearly a million hogs a year have gone from Nebraska and Iowa to West Coast plants for slaughtering. Because of the freight-rate barrier it has become virtually impossible to sell Omaha-packed meat on the West Coast."

Similar inequities in the past operated against the processing of minerals and the establishment of manufactories in the valley, thus preventing that mingled pattern of town and country which seems in all respects preferable to the pattern now prevailing, whereby population is intensely concentrated in relatively small regions separated by vast areas that are sparsely settled and inadequately developed.

Two kinds of social pressure resulted from this. One was focused on the Interstate Commerce Commission, whose rate-regulation powers should, though the task becomes immensely difficult, enable it to modify disparities toward that uniform rate which, by all logic and justice, ought to prevail. This effort had a considerable effect. Some of the more glaring injustices to South and Midwest were removed, and (mostly as a result of the war, but aided in many cases by more advantageous freight rates) there was a rapid expansion of industry in the valley after 1940. The other pressure focused on the Congress in an effort to create through Federal action those inland waterways which, by competition, would force railroads to lower and equalize their tariffs. A common feeling throughout the valley was expressed by Rufus Terral[3] when he said that "the regions of America have freight rates that are to their advantage or disadvantage according to their ability or inability to bargain with the railroads, [and] the

[2]Mr. Terral derived this example from an analysis of Missouri Valley rate discriminations made by C. E. Childs, "who formerly was the rate expert of the Omaha Chamber of Commerce, a position from which he was ousted by railroad influence," according to Mr. Terral.

[3]Op. cit.

only bargaining power the railroads recognize is the ability to ship by water instead of by rail."

So at a cost estimated at $300,000,000 (it's difficult to assign exact costs to any one use in such projects), a 6-foot channel was completed to Sioux City in 1940, and the Fort Peck reservoir was part and parcel of this development scheme too. The 6-foot channel was not completed, however, before it was generally deemed to be obsolete. A 9-foot channel was demanded in order to avoid unloading and reloading barges where the 9-foot channel ends, and this project was authorized by the Congress in 1945. But almost at once there developed a demand for a 12-foot channel all the way to Sioux City, to match those being built in the Ohio and Mississippi, the argument being that otherwise freight would have to be shifted from 12-foot to 9-foot barges at Kansas City, thus boosting shipping costs to excessive heights.

Estimates a few years ago were that a 9-foot channel would cost at least $222,000,000. A 12-foot channel would cost, of course, a great deal more. The question of whether such expenditures could be justified in terms of long-time public benefits was a tangled one which aroused a good deal of heated controversy. Certainly maintenance costs would run very high. Nevertheless, the big plans of the Army Engineers marched forward, fed by congressional appropriations through the omnibus pork-barreling river and harbors bills. New levee walls were raised, wing dikes were thrust out from the banks, stone and willow-mattress riprapping were laid down to reduce bank erosion, piles were driven deep into the river bed, dredging operations continued, and all this was done in recent years according to a master plan which in the early 1940s was given a name. It was the Pick Plan, christened after Colonel (now Lieutenant General) Lewis A. Pick, who first crystallized Army Engineer plans into a valley-wide program. Because the Engineers had been assigned primary responsibility for navigation and flood control, the Pick Plan was primarily concerned with river development toward these two ends. It originally called for construction of 22 dams located where they'd do most for navigation and flood control, and some 1,500 miles of levees. A double line of the latter would be built from Sioux City to the south, enclosing a mile-wide strip below Kansas City.

The fact that a single Federal agency had charge of both flood control and navigation was fortunate. The bureaucratic squabble which would certainly arise if two competing agencies were involved could here be avoided. Nevertheless, there were those, inside and outside the Corps, who saw conflicts in actual fact between the two kinds of river development. Flood control, they asserted, had its effectiveness reduced by channel developments. The Engineers, they went on, made a mistake when they assumed that narrowing the river in order to increase channel depths, and straightening some of the kinks, would speed the flow sufficiently to scour the bottom, thus reducing silt and sediment deposits. The scouring, it was alleged, had not sufficiently occurred, and the channel had become dangerously clogged.

Those making this argument cited figures on river flow in support of their position. The Missouri Farmers Association, for example, read into a congressional committee record (Senate Hearings on S-555, 1945, pages 102–5) charts purporting to show that at Hermann, Missouri, the river could carry 316,000 cubic feet of water per second without flooding in 1928–31, whereas in 1942 it wouldn't carry more than 193,000 c.f.s. without flooding, and by 1943 it flooded whenever the flow was more than 210,000 c.f.s. Navigation developments made the difference, the association claimed. Other studies, conducted by the Regional Committee for the Missouri Valley Authority, were reported to support this claim. The committee said flatly: "The channel has been narrowed and its carrying capacity reduced. . . ."

Analysis of the great flood of June 1947 further supported this view. On June 27 in that year the Missouri River at St. Joseph reached a height of 20.4 feet with a flow of 180,000 c.f.s., whereas in 1929 the same flow produced a height of only 15.1 feet—an increase in height of 5.3 feet for the same amount of water. On June 29 a flow of 487,000 c.f.s. produced a higher crest than 550,000 c.f.s. had done in 1944. And the U. S. Geological Survey revealed[4] that, though the 1947 flood crest on the Mississippi at St. Louis was the highest since 1844, there was actually *less* water passing the city than there had been in either 1943 or '44. At St. Louis on May 24, 1943, a flow of 840,000 c.f.s. produced a height of 38.94 feet; on April 30, 1944, a flow of 844,000 c.f.s. raised the height to 39.14; but on June 2, 1947, a flow of only 783,000 c.f.s. raised the height to 40.26.

"Someone has clogged the channel," cried the *Voice of the Valley*, official newspaper of the Regional Committee for an MVA, in its issue of September–October 1947. "There is only one answer. The carrying capacity of the channel has been reduced by those great worseners of floods—the Corps of Army Engineers."

And a Public Affairs Institute pamphlet entitled *The Big Missouri, Hope of Our West*,[5] summed up: "The result [of navigation development] has been that *more* millions of dollars of flooding damage was done in the Valley in 1947, with less peak water than in previous floods."

2

What about Irrigation? The navigation vs. flood-control argument, however, paled to insignificance when compared with the argument of navigation and control vs. agricultural irrigation. This latter was exacerbated by the fact that primary responsibility for irrigation developments in the valley was assigned to the

[4]*Water Resources Review*, July 1947.

[5]Public Affairs Institute, Report No. 2, June 1948.

Bureau of Reclamation of the U. S. Department of the Interior—
and this Bureau competes bitterly with the Army Engineers for
congressional appropriations. It was thus difficult for a disinterested observer to determine how much of each agency's planning
and propaganda was motivated by a sincere and scientific concern
for valley welfare and how much was motivated by crude bureaucratic jealousies.

Essentially the quarrel (for it often amounted to that) was over
water. Was there enough water in the Missouri Valley for both
the Reclamation and Army Engineer programs? The Engineers,
though hedging their answer with many crucial "ifs," were inclined to say "yes." The Bureau of Reclamation—at least until
recently—was inclined to answer "no." And how much Federal
water development should aim toward hydroelectric power? The
Army Engineers were notably vague in their first answer. The
Pick Plan said that electric power would be developed, but it was
not specific as to the amount. The Bureau of Reclamation, on the
other hand, presented a definite figure. This agency had long
engaged in public power developments: in connection with its
127 completed dams, 46 power stations send electricity along
6,000 miles of Bureau-built power lines. It now proposed to build
17 new power plants generating a total of 758,000 kilowatts[1] with
an annual value of $17,000,000. The proposal was part of the
Bureau's Valley Plan.

For Reclamation, too, had a plan: the Sloan Plan, after engineer
W. G. Sloan, assistant chief of the Bureau's Billings, Montana,
office. It called for 90 dams located where they'd be most useful
for irrigation purposes—that is, adjacent to fertile irrigable land
—and for a system of ditches and diversions capable of watering
4,700,000 dry acres. This would bring to 10,000,000 the total num-

[1]The Federal Power Commission has estimated that 3,000,000 kilowatts of hydroelectric generating capacity *could* be installed in the
Missouri system.

ber of acres irrigated in the valley. It also called for supplemental irrigation of 420,000 acres above Sioux City, where more water was needed. Altogether, the Bureau estimated that 9,222,000 net acre-feet of water would be required each year to service the entire scheme above Sioux City. There were signs, however, that more than this might be demanded by farmers, either because of an exceptionally prolonged or severe dry cycle or because ditches were extended to new fertile acreages. The acre-foot figure, be it noted, was *net*. It represented water that would *not* return to the river as surface drainage; the bulk of it would go, instead, into living vegetation.

Could this amount of water be so used without endangering the $222,000,000 navigation program? During a wet cycle it could be, the experts agreed. But during a dry cycle, such as occurred in the 1930s, no one seemed to know for sure. It was estimated that between 1929 and 1940 the river produced on the average about 16,200,000 acre-feet a year above Sioux City. This could be augmented by water stored during wet years behind the contemplated dams. There would be some 84,600,000 acre-feet of water storage space in the reservoirs, according to the plans, but 10,000,000 acre-feet of this must be kept empty to absorb floods. Thus 74,600,000 acre-feet of actual water would be available at the end of a wet cycle to do the navigation and irrigation jobs during the dry period. Now when the Engineers presented to the Congress their figures on a 6-foot channel, they estimated that a flow of 22,000 cubic feet per second would be needed at Sioux City. They made no exact estimate of what a 9-foot channel would require when that proposal was before the Congress, but the Reclamation people said it would require 30,000 cubic feet per second at Sioux City. This is equivalent to 14,500,000 acre-feet of water per year, "without any allowance for winter flow, for sanitation purposes or waste."[2] Add up the figures: 9,222,000 acre-feet

[2]*The Big Missouri,* op. cit.

for irrigation; 14,500,000 acre-feet for navigation: and you get a grand total of 23,722,000 acre-feet per year. The river, as we've said, produced 16,200,000 acre-feet per year during a dry cycle, or did during the 12-year period from 1929 to 1940 inclusive. The difference of 7,520,000 acre-feet per year must come from the storage reservoirs.

By this figuring, if a dry cycle lasted more than seven years there just wasn't enough water to take care of both navigation and irrigation as these two developments were then planned. Either navigation or irrigation—or both—must suffer.

Now certainly it was possible that the above figuring and its unhappy conclusion were incorrect. Controversy raged over the subject, and some technicians asserted that the picture here drawn was badly distorted. But the point is that this sort of question is a question of fact, and the most common of common sense tells us that matters of fact are *not* proper subjects of controversy. One can argue sensibly over interpretations of facts. One can argue over who should get the water if there is not enough to go around. But one can*not* argue to any reasonable effect over whether or not enough water is available. Either it is or it isn't—and the only way to find out is to take a careful, scientific look-see.

Admittedly, this was not easy to do in the Missouri Valley. Rainfall fluctuates astoundingly within small areas, with the result that the records of the Weather Bureau, whose reporting stations through this region were widely scattered, were highly inaccurate guides to the total amount of precipitation in the valley. For example, reported Rufus Terral,[3] "Mitchell and Scottsbluff, in western Nebraska, are only eight miles apart, yet each town has had nearly 1.5 inches of rain within three days' time during which the other had no rain at all." This extreme variability from mile to mile meant that many local rains went unreported by the Weather Bureau, while other strictly local rains were reported as

[3]Ibid.

general. It was therefore impossible to predict flood peaks with any consistent accuracy by projecting the available rain-gauge data. Take the already-mentioned Republican River flood of 1935. Of it the Department of Agriculture said: "The astounding peak . . . climbed far above any curves likely to have been projected on the basis of rain-gauge records within the watershed of that stream, or of neighboring streams. Even the precipitation readings for the rain that brought on the disaster do not account for the prodigious volume of water that charged down the valley; somewhere between the established gauges the rainfall must have attained intensities wholly out of line with any actual measurement." In this subhumid region, rainfall also fluctuates astoundingly from year to year in any one locality. Continued Terral: "Scottsbluff's annual rainfall was almost exactly the same in 1930 as in 1929—around 17 inches—while Mitchell's increased 50 per cent—roughly from 14 inches to 21." A variation of 50 per cent between one year and another meant that stream flows could be accurately gauged only over a long period of time. Ten- or even 20-year averages from gauging stations meant little in the western portion of the Kansas Basin, and they meant but slightly more on the lower portions of the Kaw and the Missouri. As Terral pointed out, the minimum flow of the Missouri was once estimated to be twice the flow which actually occurred during the great drought of the '30s.

This poverty of necessary planning data was further emphasized by the 1951 floods. A knowledge of what peak flows to expect would seem indispensable to successful flood-control planning as well as to plans for water storage, since inadequate control structures sometimes prove worse than none at all. Dams which break, levees which break or are overtopped (if overtopped, they often break), reservoirs which fill so long before the crisis is past that their gates must be opened during the height of the flood, these may vastly augment flood damage. Yet the Corps of Engineers' plans for the Kansas Basin, immense though they seemed, would not, according to the Corps itself, have provided full protection against the 1951 flood had all the works been in place.[4] At Manhattan the actual discharge would have exceeded the planned discharge by approximately 110,000 c.f.s., and the recommended works along the Kaw there would have been over-topped by 2 or 3 feet. At Topeka the discharge "would have exceeded the safe discharge by about 70,000 c.f.s. and the existing or recommended works on one side of the river or the other would have been overtopped by 1 foot." The capacity of existing works at Lawrence would have been exceeded by about 130,000 c.f.s., and they would have been overtopped by about 3 feet. Even at Kansas City, for whose benefit the control program was chiefly planned (and with what seemed to some upstream citizens a callous disregard for their rights and interests), the flood would have reached the top of existing and recommended works along the Kaw. Here, however, the crest would have been reduced by as much as 5 feet and damages of $100,000,000 would have been prevented, according to estimates by the Engineers.

Prior to 1951, flood-control plans for the Kansas Basin had been based on data from the 1903 flood. The storm which produced that flood was shifted on the map so that its maximum intensity coincided with the most critical points in the Kansas system; in terms of this hypothetical storm, considerably enlarged, the control plans were made. But suppose the same procedure were followed with regard to the flood-producing 1951 storm—as indeed it has been. A transposition of the 1951 storm just a few miles north of where it actually occurred would have increased the peak flow at Kansas City by *one third!* It seems probable that the damage at Kansas City in that case, and despite the full instal-

[4]Information in presentation by Colonel L. J. Lincoln, Kansas City District Engineer, to Missouri Basin Inter-Agency Committee, Topeka, Kansas, December 14, 1951.

lation of the Pick Plan of that date, would have been approximately as great as actually occurred in '51; and we now know that a flood of these proportions can be expected to occur within a normal lifetime!

All the above emphasizes that the quest for needed data was difficult in our valley—but it was obviously the only way we could really answer the question of How Much Water. Argument until doomsday would not answer it, no matter how eloquent it be or how passionate. Nor would argument answer the other questions of fact which had been raised—the question, for instance, of whether navigation developments increased flood hazards, or the question of how much (if any) reduction of monster floods could be achieved by soil-conservation practices on the uplands. The only thing to do was go find out. Why, then, did we not do so in effective fashion?

A chief reason was that the acquisition of different sets of facts was the responsibility of different Federal agencies, each with its own budget, its own specific terms of reference from the Congress, and its own *esprit de corps* which, when it inhibited needed co-operation, did at least as much harm as good. It is clear from the above discussion, for example, that a great expansion in scientific weather reporting was needed to provide absolutely basic data for valley engineering. But weather reporting was not the responsibility of the Army Engineers or the Bureau of Reclamation. It was the responsibility of the U. S. Weather Bureau —and any considerable expansion of this agency's activities in the region might conceivably reduce the activities of other agencies, since the total Federal budget for any one year had (even though some people didn't think so) definite limits. Similarly with the U. S. Public Health Service and the U. S. Soil Conservation Service, two agencies whose data and whose planning abilities were indispensable to the wisest use of valley water.

In recent years, however, more concerted efforts *have* been made to get at the facts and to use them in integrated planning. Let us examine them.

3

The Wedlock of Pick and Sloan: Holy or Unholy?   A chief incitement to new integrative efforts was the pattern provided by the Tennessee Valley Authority, a pattern which was of course variously viewed but whose influence was undoubted. Some saw it as a shining example for the Missouri Valley to follow—with necessary modifications. Others saw it as the darkest of threats, to be avoided at all costs—including the not inconsiderable expense of lobbies and widespread propaganda. But no one seriously concerned with Missouri Valley problems looked upon TVA with indifference or failed to note that its undeniable successes derived, in large part, from the fact that TVA was a *single* agency, a government corporation set up to do a unified, multiple-purpose, valley-wide job. It was clear that the Tennessee Valley could never have been developed as it was if a half dozen Federal agencies had operated as sovereign powers on a half dozen portions of the total valley problem.

Seeing this, popular criticism of Missouri Valley plans became increasingly vociferous. Many and loud were the cries that important interests, carefully guarded in the multiple-purpose planning of TVA, were either ignored completely or insufficiently served by the Missouri projects of Reclamation and the Engineers. Why so little low-cost electric power in an area which needs so much? What about the use of streams and reservoirs as recreation areas? What about public health with its close dependence on safe and abundant water supplies? To what extent were these matters considered when dams and reservoirs were designed? Obviously they were not, in many cases, considered at all. And why weren't they? Because valley development was proceeding piecemeal. Let's integrate! cried influential voices. Why not eliminate the frustrating, irritating, thoroughly wasteful inter-agency competitions in our own valley? Since specialized knowledge and talent are valuable only to the extent that they are parts of a *total* effort, why not pool them in a single agency through which a total effort can be made? In short, why not set up an MVA?

Senator James E. Murray of Montana saw no reason why not and introduced a bill whose passage would accomplish that purpose. His proposal was promptly supported by the American Federation of Labor, the Congress of Industrial Organizations, the National Farmers Union, President Roosevelt, the St. Louis *Post-Dispatch,* and most of the leading political liberals in the valley. It was as promptly opposed by the river-navigation interests, private utility corporations, many private contracting firms (TVA did its own building instead of letting fat contracts), the Kansas City *Star,* and most of the leading political conservatives of the valley. The issue was joined, and the noise was great.

The immediate result could have been predicted by anyone aware of the "common enemy" device for achieving social unity: it was an abrupt marriage of convenience between the Pick and Sloan plans. However seriously Reclamation and the Engineers might disagree, they were as one in their opposition to an authority in which their identities would be lost—and this opposition provided common ground for the so-called "Omaha Compromise" of 1944. The wedding took place just eight weeks after the Murray bill was introduced and four weeks after President Roosevelt sent a special message to Congress calling for the creation of Columbia, Arkansas, and Missouri Valley Authorities. The "vs." between Pick and Sloan was replaced, or hidden, by a hyphen: the ill-matched couple was now the Pick-Sloan Plan, and the Congress subsequently blessed the union with appropriate legislation.

In effect, the new plan as approved by the Congress was a simple combination of the two original schemes. Altogether 107 new dams and reservoirs were proposed, including nearly all of Pick's original 22 and Sloan's original 90—and this despite the fact that, before the Omaha meeting, each agency was loudly certain that some of the other's proposals were wholly unjustified. Pick's 1,500 miles of levees were included, and so were Sloan's 4,700,000 acres of new irrigation. Sloan's hydroelectric-power proposals were included, and so, of course, was the virtually completed 9-foot navigation channel from Sioux City to the mouth of the Missouri. In June of 1948 the Engineers had under actual construction 6 reservoirs, 15 local flood-protection projects, and 3 navigation projects at a total completion cost then estimated at $796,000,000, while the Reclamation Bureau had under construction 17 reservoirs with associated irrigation works with a completion cost of $595,000,000. Total cost of the authorized six-year program was then estimated at $6,360,000,000.

Of these vast developments a not inconsiderable portion lay within the Kansas River Basin. A large dam at Kanopolis, Kansas, was completed in 1950, and a lake of 3,500 acres has formed behind it. Another in Harlan County, Nebraska, primarily for flood control but including irrigation, was completed and placed in operation in 1951. Four other dams were under construction, three on the Republican and one on the Smoky Hill 80 miles above the Kanopolis fill. Construction of 10 additional dams was authorized by the Congress, and a still additional 18 were proposed before the '51 flood. Altogether, if these plans had been completed, 34 reservoirs in the Kansas Basin would now be holding approximately 7,100,000 acre-feet of water, of which 1,130,000 would be available for irrigation and 1,400,000 would be assigned to conservation. If the full planned potential had been realized, more than 300,000 new acres of land in subhumid

Kansas and Nebraska and Colorado would now be irrigated, and 1,200 kilowatts of electric power would be generated by the Harlan County Dam for an area now notably deficient in such power.

But as we've already noted, even this vast development whereby some scores of thousands of acres of farmland would be permanently flooded to provide irrigation water and to prevent recurrent floods downstream, even this was proved inadequate by the 1951 catastrophe, according to the Army Engineers. True, General Pick asserted at the height of the flood that all this would have been prevented had his plan been fully in effect—an assertion which was given banner heads in the newspapers of the flood-stricken areas and which he never retracted. But his assertion was obviously never accepted as valid by his own staff. Within weeks after the raging waters went down that year the Engineers had greatly expanded their plans. They now proposed to build in the Kansas Basin 22 additional reservoirs and a number of local protection projects (levees and the like), expanding to approximately 7,600,000 acre-feet the capacity for "retention and control of flood waters at strategic points to secure the most widespread benefit from reduction of flood losses in both rural and urban damage centers."[1] These additional projects would come close to doubling the total cost of the control program, boosting it to some $700,000,000 for the basin—but the Engineers said they were sure that *this* time their plans were big enough and that the cost could be thoroughly justified. They estimated that had this truly adequate program been in effect it would almost have paid for itself during the single flood storm of July '51, for it would then have prevented damages "in the order of $645,000,000." Tremendous indeed by this figuring would be the saving during the next fifty years if the flood cycle of the last half century were repeated, and especially if there were added to it

[1]Colonel Lincoln, op. cit.

that monster flood whose possibility was revealed by transposing the '51 storm just a few miles northward.

Helping to guide all these developments in terms of general policy was a Missouri Basin Inter-Agency Committee, established in 1945, shortly after the joining of Pick and Sloan. Designed to mitigate criticism of the plan, if not to remove its basic causes, the committee reviewed problems which arose among the various and still-independent Federal programs. It was a voluntary committee, originally composed of representatives of the Departments of Army, Commerce, Interior, and Agriculture, the Federal Power Commission, and five Missouri Valley state governors.[2] The first chairman was Pick, who was succeeded by Sloan of Reclamation; Sloan in turn was succeeded by Gladwin Young of the Department of Agriculture. The meetings provided a forum for the 24 Federal bureaus concerned with various phases of the plan. These 24 included the Weather Bureau, the Forest Service, the Rural Electrification Administration, the National Park Service, the Soil Conservation Service, and the Public Health Service. Meetings of the committee were public, and private citizens were free to participate in discussions. Thus, as we've said, data-gathering activities became more extensive and better co-ordinated than they formerly were; and citizens of the region had, in the committee meetings, an instrument through which to communicate their opinions and prejudices directly to those heading up the work.

By the fall of 1949, W. G. Sloan of Reclamation could announce with justifiable pride[3] that "all over the Missouri Basin construction work is proceeding at an unprecedented rate," that "practically all major features under construction are well ahead of schedule," and that "all the key structures in the program are

[2]State representation was rotated among the ten states in the valley, only five being represented at any one time.

[3]In a paper presented November 30, 1949, in Omaha.

either under way or will be started within the next year." The Fort Randall and Garrison dams on the main stem of the Missouri were "so far along," he said, "that by the year 1953 or 1954 people living along the river from Yankton to Kansas City can be assured that the disastrous floods which have been recurring so frequently of late will be a thing of the past." He added that "with the completion of the Harlan County Dam and the protection works now under way in the vicinity of Kansas City, that city can be assured of complete flood protection within three or four years."

Three years later, in the summer of 1952, Inter-Agency issued a handsome illustrated pamphlet, printed on glossy stock and entitled *The Missouri River Basin Development Program.* Designed for popular consumption, it was a glowing account of work accomplished and work planned. It said that "the program as now planned proposes:

1. More than 100 multipurpose reservoirs on the Missouri River and its tributaries with a capacity of 110,000,000 acre-feet of water for various uses.
2. Irrigation of more than 5,000,000 additional acres of land, and supplemental water for approximately 2,000,000 acres now receiving an inadequate supply.
3. Application of soil and moisture conservation measures on nearly 340,000,000 acres of farms, ranches, range lands, and forests to gain extensive benefits in erosion and sedimentation prevention, flood control, and improved agricultural production.
4. Hydroelectric plants having an ultimate installed generating capacity of 3,200,000 kilowatts and an annual output of more than 13,000,000,000 kilowatt-hours.[4]

[4]It is naïve, however, to suppose that the Missouri Basin program *does,* in actual fact, propose to install hydroelectric plants with the generating capacity listed above, thus realizing the full possibilities estimated by the Federal Power Commission several years ago. One hesitates to say that this statement concerning "ultimate installed generating capacity" was designed to deceive the public, but it certainly has that effect. Meanwhile our privately owned "business-managed taxpaying"

5. Control of floods by storage capacity exclusively for flood control in most of the reservoirs in the development program, providing for elimination or considerable reduction of flood damage on 5,000,000 acres of valley lands. Local flood protection works at many cities, both large and small, shielding high-value areas subject to flooding. Agricultural levees along the Missouri River from Sioux City, Iowa, to the mouth, protecting 1,400,000 acres of fertile farmland.

6. Stabilization works to prevent erosion of valuable agricultural land, bridges and approaches, and industrial centers, and to establish a navigation channel up to Sioux City.

7. Controlled streamflow, through reservoir retentions and releases, to improve municipal, industrial, and domestic water supplies and alleviate stream pollution.

8. Improvement of fish and wildlife habitat and construction of new features to encourage such development.

9. Construction of recreational facilities at reservoir sites, in forests, and in other suitable areas to utilize recreational potentials.

10. Provision of statistical, informational and other aids to agriculture, industry and business, to promote the far-reaching gains and growth to be expected from full development of the Basin's resources."

The grandeur of this engineering stirred the imagination. It should greatly augment the wealth and reduce the flood risks of the valley. It could hardly fail to inaugurate a new economic era

---

public utilities know full well that this hydroelectric potential will never be realized as long as the present administrative chaos prevails in the valley, that the very desire to do so is absent from top policy-making councils, and that the chances of developing a public opinion which might force the needed projects became further remote when Big Business interests, having long controlled most of our agencies of mass communication, became in 1953 the dominant force in the Federal executive as well. The 1,200 kw. "planned potential" for the Harlan County Dam, for instance, was quietly eliminated as the dam was completed, and at this writing no *hydroelectric development whatever* was planned for the entire Kansas Basin!

across the plains. Nevertheless, criticism of the plan and pressures for an MVA continued.[5]

For despite the attempts at co-ordination of the program, there remained people who asserted that the Pick-Sloan Plan came about as close to a truly integrated development program as the United Nations came to a true world government. They found Reclamation and the Engineers occupying, in the new setup, positions almost precisely analogous to those of Russia and the United States in the UN—two great sovereign powers who, behind all the window dressing, would admit of no law but their own. They claimed that the Inter-Agency Committee was about as effective a peacemaker as the UN's Security Council, and for the same reason—the committee could act (in so far as it could act at all) only through unanimous consent of the major Federal members. Thus each "sovereign state" had veto powers, and when these were exercised on truly crucial issues (as they always were), the issues were referred to Washington. Ultimately they might go to the Congress (a notorious controversy over the height of the Garrison Dam in North Dakota went there), and this, in view of the pressure groupings and the competing lobbies, was all too closely analogous to going to war. Certainly the Congress was ill equipped to solve engineering problems in other than political terms.

The committee was far better designed for logrolling among its sovereign members than for co-operative planning toward intelligently conceived ends. But even in this design it operated to the acute dissatisfaction of those agencies that lacked the powerful, tightly organized lobbies through which both Reclamation and the Corps of Engineers—and particularly the latter—could manipulate legislation. The Department of Agriculture, for instance, was presumed to represent the interests of some six million economic units; the department's programs actually involved most of these

[5]The latter pressures seemed now somewhat weaker than formerly.

millions, of whom a fair proportion were in the valley. The Army
Engineers, on the other hand, represented with directness the
special interests of only a few thousand people as they let their
fat contracts and opposed all efforts toward genuine valley-wide
integration. Yet the plans of the Engineers marched rapidly for-
ward, as we've seen, sustained by enormous congressional appropriations, while most of Agriculture's plan for the valley lay
inert on paper. As an example, Reclamation and the Engineers
had for the fiscal year 1952 appropriations of approximately
$254,000,000 specifically earmarked for phases of the Pick-Sloan
Plan; Agriculture had appropriations of only $33,000,000 for *all*
its conservation work in the valley, consisting of all land and
water functions of the department, including research and soil
surveys. Obviously the upstream phases of watershed development, with which Agriculture was chiefly concerned, were receiving little effective attention from the Congress, though there
had been some effort in recent years to promote into the popular
consciousness the notion that the grand design for the valley
should now be called the Pick-Sloan-Young Plan (the "Young"
standing for the field representative of the Secretary of Agriculture, Gladwin Young), as though the Engineers, Reclamation,
and Agriculture were now on equal footing.

Among those highly critical of present arrangements was the
Hoover Commission, established to study and make recommendations concerning the organization of the executive branch of
Federal government. The Commission's "Task Force on Natural
Resources" (Appendix L) contained a careful review of Missouri
Valley developments through June of 1948. The Task Force found
that "the most conspicuous missing parts" in the present plans
were: "(a) A means of considering the over-all social and economic objectives of the region (toward which all present efforts
should be directed); a means of evaluating the several programs
in relation to those objectives; and an instrument for integrating

the program on some basis other than Federal agency compromise. (b) A means of continuing consideration of regional development and conservation problems, prepared for study, recommendations, and action on them as they arise."

The Task Force found the present Inter-Agency Committee wholly unable to supply these "missing parts," and for the following reasons:

a. [The committee] has no authority . . . no capacity for decision . . . [and] no staff for the study of problems concerning two or more of the programs.
b. It does not have an over-all social and economic program, nor the means of formulating one . . .
c. [The] committee is not equipped to carry on the continuing research in industrial engineering problems . . . [needed in] a program of industrial encouragement. There is no provision for undertaking the complex task of balancing manufacturing and agriculture in the valley.
d. The committee is not at present an agency for anticipating general problems, it is a forum for harmonizing established programs.

Similar criticisms were made by virtually every disinterested student of the prevailing administrative setup, including members of the President's Water Resources Policy Commission. In its "A Water Policy for the American People" (Volume I of the report, issued in 1950) the Commission complained that "there is today no single uniform Federal policy governing comprehensive development of water and land resources.

"Some statutes of uniform application separately control various aspects or functions," the report continued. "Others are geared to a comprehensive approach, but focus attention on individual projects, specific areas, or single river basins.[6] In so far as it may now be achieved, therefore, comprehensive development of river basins must depend upon a number of statutes, passed at different

[6]This refers to the Tennessee River primarily; there is no such focus on the Kansas Basin, of course.

times, devoted to individual segments of basin development, and administered by separate executive agencies."[7]

The Commission went on to state a "framework of principles" which, since none of them was adequately applied in our valley, was a series of implied criticisms of present policies and practices. These "principles" expressed:

1. The importance of clearly defined regional and national goals which water resources programs will be designed to achieve.
2. The necessity of planning for a river basin as a whole instead of having a patchwork of plans by separate agencies for separate purposes.
3. The importance of a simple procedure for determining whether the money to be invested in a river basin program will be well spent.
4. The necessity for a system of repayment designed to treat alike all who enjoy the advantages of Federal investment.
5. The need for placing the annual financing of water resources undertakings on a river basin program basis and for recognizing the annual renewable resources investment program as a stabilizing factor in the economy.
6. The importance of providing those who prepare the plans for the Nation's river basins with all the knowledge which is required to assure good plans.
7. The necessity for applying sound management principles to our watersheds, to the ground waters which replenish our supplies, and to the floodwaters which, harnessed, confer a host of blessings.
8. The importance of utilizing all these services which water resources offer in such a way as to contribute to the continued building of a strong Nation.

Such sober criticisms as these, however, conveyed nothing of the emotional heat of valley dwellers whenever they came into harsh frictional contact with prevailing bureaucratic arrangements. Such contacts were increasingly frequent, for Pick-Sloan

[7]Which meant that truly comprehensive development could not be achieved at all.

was fed an ever-richer diet of pork after the end of World War II and marched on inexorably. A more adequate conception of the tone of the argument can be gained from the statements of Leslie A. Miller when he spoke his own "unofficial" mind. Mr. Miller, a former governor of Wyoming, was chairman of that Hoover Commission Task Force whose report we've quoted, and in the *Saturday Evening Post* for May 14, 1949, he angrily charged that "billions of dollars were being squandered on duplicating, badly engineered projects" by the Army Engineers and the Bureau of Reclamation. Estimating that the cost of water-resources-development projects "now in the construction and planning stages" over the country as a whole amounted to $52,706,500,000, Mr. Miller made the following four points:

1. The two agencies are so violently jealous of each other that an extravagant and wholly senseless competition has sprung up. They will encroach on each other's territory and stake out rival claims simply to beat out each other in the race to construct expensive projects.
2. In their indecent zeal to extend their empires, both agencies are guilty of underestimating—apparently deliberately—the cost of projects they propose to build. This . . . has the effect of bamboozling Congress into easy acquiescence. For instance, if the whole $52,706,500,000 water-development program should be approved by Congress, the entire job when completed, on the basis of past performances by the Engineers and the Bureau of Reclamation, probably would cost more than double that figure.
3. Both agencies stoop to deception in furtherance of their efforts to stake out claims on projects.
4. Both agencies are guilty of brazen and pernicious lobbying to achieve their ends.[8]

[8]General Lewis A. Pick, questioned about this article before the Sub-Committee to Study Civil Works, of the Committee on Public Works, House of Representatives, March 1952, inserted in the record of hearings a "detailed analysis" of it. The "analysis" consisted of a point-by-point denial, unsupported by convincing evidence, that the charges

Herbert Hoover wrote a preface to this article, saying: "Opposition to effective corrective measures is already rampant. . . . The battlers of the bureaus must be overcome by sheer force of public opinion if our free system is to be saved for future generations."

Perhaps here is as good a place as any in which to review briefly the historical development of the civil functions of the Army

---

were true. Reclamation and the Engineers are jealous of one another? Replied General Pick: "The agencies are not jealous of each other." They encroach on each other's territory? Replied General Pick: "They do not encroach on each other's territory." Billions have been wasted on "duplicating" and "badly engineered" projects? Replied General Pick: "None [of the appropriation] has been spent on 'duplicating projects' . . . and rather than being 'badly engineered' the engineering has been of the highest quality." The costs of projects are deliberately underestimated? Replied General Pick: "The Corps of Engineers denies flatly that it deliberately underestimates costs." The Corps is guilty of "brazen and pernicious" lobbying? Replied General Pick: "The Corps of Engineers does not engage in lobbying activities." The Engineers "have a whole string of lobbies behind them, including the aggressive Mississippi Valley Association and the wealthy, influential National Rivers and Harbors Congress"? Replied General Pick blandly: "[When] those organizations are lobbies, then they are lobbies for projects and programs and not for any Federal agencies to which such projects and programs are assigned by Congress"—a distinction which may be too subtle to be grasped by minds accustomed to blunt honesty. General Pick went on to say that "the Corps of Engineers has no particular relationship with waterway organizations of this kind"—a piece of sophistry tantamount to deliberate falsehood. The Corps *as* a corps may not have any "particular relationship" with the Rivers and Harbors Congress, but all Corps officers engaged in rivers and harbors work are *ex officio members of it!* And by General Pick's own admission this organization *may* lobby for "projects and programs" that just *happen* to be covered by congressional bills of appropriation for the Corps of Engineers.

Engineers. Offhand it must seem strange that the Army should be charged with rivers and harbors developments; if such civil functions *must* be assigned to an armed service, the uninitiate might expect the Navy to be chosen. The primary distinction between Army and Navy, after all, is that the former fights on solid ground while the latter fights on and over water. But apparently in this instance no really conscious choice was made: neither the legislative nor the executive branches of our government actually planned the growth of the Engineers to their present seemingly invincible and omnipotent position. The process seems to have been started almost inadvertently and to have continued by inertia through a series of legal and administrative expediencies.

The organization of a Corps of Engineers was authorized by the Continental Congress in 1775, and this Corps continued in existence until 1783, when it was disbanded. In 1802 a new Corps was established by congressional act, to consist of five officers and ten cadets: they were to "constitute a Military Academy" at West Point, New York. A few years later, Corps headquarters were moved to Washington, but the Engineers remained in charge of West Point—the first professional engineering school in the United States—until 1866, and to this day the top-ranking students of the academy are called "engineers."

The decision to concern the Engineers with civil as well as military functions was made by administrators who obviously consulted their convenience more than their wisdom in this matter. The democracy espoused by Jefferson was justly suspicious of that hunger for power, that tendency toward despotism, which seems to be inherent in the very structure of armies and in the psychology of those who are attracted to military pursuits. Yet it was Jefferson who laid the foundations for the Corps of Engineers' career as a civil engineering agency—and when the Federal government instituted what, by the standards of those days, was a vast program of internal improvements in the 1820s, the Corps of

Engineers was the only competent body to whom actual work could be assigned. During that decade the Engineers undertook projects to improve the navigation of the Ohio and Mississippi rivers, to build the Chesapeake and Ohio Canal, and to continue the Cumberland Road. They also began operations on the Missouri River, the initial activity, in 1824, consisting of the removal of snags as an aid to navigation. Rivers and harbors work was assigned generally to the Engineers by congressional act in 1852, and thirty years later the Engineers initiated bank-stabilization work on the Missouri—work which has never ceased. In 1917 the Congress added flood-control work to the Engineers' repertory, and in 1936 the Flood Control Act (an omnibus bill which rolls on and on and on) still more definitely assigned flood-control work, for the nation as a whole, to the Corps. By this time the Corps was solidly, even immovably, established, with reference to its civil functions, as the United States Engineer Department, and by the late 1940s some 40,000 civilian employees worked under the over-all supervision of about 200 Army Engineer officers. The fact that the bulk of the Corps' engineering work was done by civilian professionals was obscured from the popular gaze because only officers spoke for the Corps in public.

By this time, too, the Corps had grown into by far the most powerful bureau in government. As a military unit, responsible to the Chief of Staff and ultimately to the President as Commander-in-Chief, the Corps carried out military construction, military engineering supply, and military engineering training programs. But as a civil construction agency the Corps was on paper responsible *directly* to the Secretary of War (since 1947, the Secretary of the Army), who "as a matter of fact . . . exercises little, if any, real supervision of review over the conduct of Engineer civil functions."[9] In effect the Corps in its civil functions was responsi-

[9]*Muddy Waters, The Army Engineers and the Nation's Rivers*, by Arthur Maass. Cambridge, Mass.; Harvard University Press, 1951.

ble directly and almost exclusively to the Congress, for it often demonstrated its ability to ignore or contradict the desires of the executive branch by manipulating special-interest pressures upon the legislative.[10]

A case in point is the long, hard, and ultimately futile effort of Franklin Roosevelt to bring order out of the chaos of Federal natural-resource-development programs by use of an over-all planning board. Every step of the way he was opposed by the Army Engineers, whose chief weapons were two: (1) the so-called rivers and harbors bloc of the Congress of the United States; (2) the National Rivers and Harbors Congress, a special-interest pressure group which derives enormous power from the fact that its membership actually comprises many of those who are the objects of its pressure, namely U.S. senators and representatives[11] and all Army Engineer officers engaged in rivers and harbors work, as well as representatives of state and local governments, industrial organizations, trade associations, labor unions, and private contractors. Against this formidable opposition the President was unable to secure the revision of laws and the legislative mandate for establishment of a permanent planning board, required to bring the Engineers into the same relation with the White House as all other Federal bureaus have, and to

[10]In 1934 the Secretary of War, Mr. Dern, stated the situation bluntly in a letter to the President, in which he opposed efforts of the latter to combine in a single master plan all elements of river planning. Mr. Dern seems to have had as a primary concern the protection of the Army Engineers' privileged position *against* the President of whose Cabinet he was a member, and he spoke of "noteworthy and praiseworthy achievements of the Corps of Engineers, acting in *pursuance of law as an agency of the legislative branch*"! The letter is quoted at length by Arthur Maass, op. cit.

[11]These are designated "honorary members," but this doesn't mean they are inactive in the organization. On the contrary, they participate fully, even serving as presiding officers.

provide for truly integrative, truly comprehensive river-basin planning.

He did manage to obtain, on what proved to be a temporary basis, a National Resources Planning Board as part of his reorganized Executive Office in 1939. With this imperfect device he sought to make more rational and less vulnerable to selfishness the planning procedure for water resources. Bringing to bear the full weight of his office, he ordered the recalcitrant Engineers to submit their water-project proposals to the Executive Office for review by the NRPB and the Bureau of the Budget prior to submitting them to the Congress. Only thus, of course, could the Engineers' proposals be brought in line with the over-all program of the administration. But, alas, this was but a minor obstacle to the astute political generals of the Engineers, who managed easily to circumvent or surmount it as they continued their triumphant marches upon the Federal treasury. At no time did the Congress of the United States (its rivers and harbors bloc consistently aided by the Republican minority) give much weight to the wishes of the Executive Office when these conflicted with those of the Corps of Engineers,[12] and finally, in 1943, the rivers and harbors bloc, joined by the solidly voting Republicans, managed to destroy the Planning Board altogether. In this manner was lost

[12]Instructive is an analysis made by Arthur Maass (op. cit.) of the period from January 1941 to August 1948. During this period 42 reports out of 914 from the USED (the Army Engineers in their civil role) were held by the Executive Office to be wholly out of line with the total administrative program. On each of these the Corps of Engineers made to the Congress its own report, favorable, of course, and by August of '48 the Congress had approved 36 (or more than 85 per cent) of them. During this same period the Executive Office had partially disapproved of 76 proposed Engineer projects, and of these 62 had been authorized by the Congress up to August of '48, while only 7 had been abandoned by the Engineers or had been considered by the Congress and disapproved. The 7 remaining proposals had not, up to that time, been acted on.

the best opportunity America had yet had for developing an administrative structure consistent with nature's requirements and hence with the basic principles of wise river planning.

Strengthened by this victory over the Roosevelt administration, the Corps of Engineers and its powerful friends were able to dispose of the "threat" posed by Hoover Commission recommendations under the Truman administration in the late 1940s. These recommendations—to be discussed more fully later—called for a removal from the Army Engineers of all their civil functions, transferring these to exclusively civilian agencies definitely integrated with the executive branch. The Task Force on Natural Resources knew well what to expect from those who had a vested interest in the status quo. "Perhaps the most imposing argument against transferring the civil functions of the Corps of Engineers to another agency is found in the intense opposition with which any such proposal is likely to be met," said the Task Force report. "There is no need to emphasize the powerful local and congressional support for the Corps . . . The history of past reorganization efforts reveals the difficulties encountered when measures have been proposed involving any change whatsoever in the civil functions of the Army Engineers. As one writer[13] has said, 'the civil functions of the Army Corps of Engineers constitute a veritable Rock of Gibraltar against all executive attempts to introduce any organizational integration of flood control and river development with land-use, irrigation, and electric power activities of other Federal agencies.'" Nevertheless, Task Force members were unanimous in their recommendations, and when these were acted upon by the Hoover Commission itself their essential elements were approved by it. Of the twelve commissioners, only two dissented from the majority view, and one of

[13]The writer was Avery Leiserson in his article, "Political Limitations of Executive Reorganization," in *American Political Science Review*, Vol. 41, page 73, 1947.

these two was Senator John L. McClellan of Arkansas, who at the time was president of the National Rivers and Harbors Congress. He was also chairman of the Senate Committee on Expenditures, to which the Hoover report was referred. In the congressional battle which followed, Senator McClellan fought effectively on behalf of the Engineers and their powerful friends, and it is possible that the effort to "save" the Corps as a civil construction agency became the chief obstacle to the Hoover reorganization plans in general. Herbert Hoover, appearing before Senator McClellan's committee, warned that committee that the pressure of the Engineers "is one you must resist if you are ever to reorganize the Government [for] success in this drive will result in every other quarter of Government putting on similar campaigns [and] we will get nowhere."

It was on behalf of a *general* reorganization bill, sponsored by President Truman, that Herbert Hoover spoke. The act called for was to have no exceptions from Commission recommendations, and it was to be a permanent law rather than one which expired in a few years. Its provisions were similar to those of earlier acts in that any plans for reorganizing the executive branch, submitted by the President, would become law unless vetoed by *both* Houses of Congress within sixty days. The rivers and harbors bloc fought first to exempt the Corps of Engineers from provisions of the bill. Failing in that, after a stubborn battle, they managed to insert in the Senate bill a clause whereby any plan submitted by the President would become law only if approved by *both* Houses—departing, in other words, from the two-House veto required in earlier bills. To this one-House veto the House of Representatives refused at first to agree, and the Senate-House conference committee remained deadlocked for a month, at the end of which time it was the House that surrendered. All that the House conferees were able to obtain from the Senate by way of compromise was a provision that any resolution of veto passed by either House must be approved by an absolute majority of all members instead of a simple majority of those present and voting. Thus was assured the defeat of every major reorganization plan submitted to the Congress up to 1952 as the President sought to carry out the Hoover Commission recommendations.

4

The Battle for the Blue Valley   Of all the scenic beauties witnessed by Frémont during his journeys of exploration in 1842 and '43, none evoked more lyrical descriptions than those of the lower Blue Valley; the beauties he saw were still visible in 1952, though marred here and there by a century of the white man's exploitive settlement. From Marysville to Manhattan, the Blue flowed through a rich bottomland (even in the dry year of '52 some of the corn made 80 bushels per acre) 45 miles long and two to five miles wide. On either hand rose hills through whose steep flanks—their wide sweeps of grass interrupted by clumps of low-growing sumac—protruded level ridges of white stone, the compacted bones of an ancient sea life. Every so often these hills were parted by side valleys formed by creeks fingering to the west or east from the main stem of the Blue, and these narrow valleys were of a special beauty. Along the river and the creeks grew willows and majestic cottonwoods and elms and oaks—and on some of the north slopes of the side valleys there were thick woods, mostly of scrub oak. Otherwise the hills bore no trees, or very few, so that there was about them a sense of loneliness beneath the skies.

Before good roads and improved automobiles enlarged the trading territories of the larger towns, virtually destroying the trade of crossroads stores and the tiniest villages, the Blue Valley was divided into tightly contained sociological segments. The people of one side valley were strangers to those of the next valley, and this separation continued with slight modification down onto the main stem's flood plain, which thus became vertebral. For the first two or three generations of settlement there was even a language barrier between them quite often. When the Swedes came into the valley they formed their own settlement and continued there the worship, the ways of life, and the language of the Old Country; many of them never learned English. When the Germans came into a different part of the valley they did the same. The two settlements had little to do with one another, or with the New Englanders and other "older" Americans who were their neighbors. This sociological pattern was dominant through most of the first quarter of the twentieth century, and many elements of it remained even after half the century, crowded with mechanical progress, had crushed larger and larger portions of our country into a single All-American Way.

Particularly interesting and lovely in all its aspects in 1952 was the Swedish community known as Mariadahl, some twenty miles north of Manhattan, a community whose center was a Lutheran church organized by one Reverend John A. Johnson in 1863. This was the oldest Lutheran church west of the Missouri, and its building, dating from 1866, was among the most beautiful. Built of native limestone, it seemed to rise as a natural growth out of the soil on which it stood. In its yard, to the north, was one of the oldest cemeteries in the state, where lay the grandfathers and great-grandfathers of present inhabitants, and to the south, down a walk deep-shaded by two rows of red cedars, was the limestone parsonage, whose lines were as simple and restfully balanced as those of the church. Across the road, to the east, stood an orphanage, also of limestone, and above the orphanage rose a lime-ridged hill, while behind the churchyard, to the west, flowed the Blue River. The river curved there, and from its eastern bank during the flood of '51 had fallen many cubic yards of rich black earth. In '52 the ravages of that flood were also evident in up-rooted trees lying at the edge of the stream and in huge masses of driftwood piled against the piers of a bridge a little way up-stream. Otherwise there was in this scene a perfect peace, with no hint of violence—a self-contained peace transplanted, yet flourishing, from another time and another land. Here seemed to be a permanent beauty only mildly threatened, if at all, by a river of change.

The appearance of peace was deceptive in 1952, however. The river's rage of '51 was more in keeping with the valley's mood in '52, and however mild seemed the September air, there was a hint of violence in it, born of man's conflicting responses to the river's challenge. The beauty of the landscape was far from permanent. It had instead a meager future, being sentenced to early death by drowning.

This sentence had been obtained by the Corps of Engineers in 1938, when the Congress approved the Engineers' desire to construct a large flood-control dam across the Blue just below the mouth of Tuttle Creek (a tiny creek flowing into the river from the west) and only a few miles north of Manhattan. Through fourteen years, execution of the sentence had been delayed by appeals and arguments and political pressures from the sentenced valley as well as by what seemed at times to be indecision on the part of the Engineers themselves. Certainly the design of the proposed dam underwent several modifications during this period as emphases were shifted among the dam's multiple purposes,[1] a fact which did nothing to convince the people of the Blue Valley that the Engineers knew with precision what should be done, or even that they particularly cared what should be done

---

[1]According to some critics, the "multiple-purpose" dam whose values seemed so abundantly demonstrated by TVA became in the hands of the Engineers simply a device for obscuring the unfavorable cost-benefit ratio which candor would discover in many of their proposals.

so long as they could satisfy their passion for Big Engineering. In this, the people of the valley were no doubt unfair to the Engineers: the latter insisted that Tuttle Creek was necessary to defend Topeka and Kansas City against floods, that it was a key structure in the entire Pick Plan of mutually reinforcing reservoirs throughout the Missouri Valley, and that whatever changes had been made in design had been merely changes of detail.

The flood of '51, of course, gave a sudden impetus to Tuttle Creek. Angry waters had not subsided before the Engineers were proclaiming in newspaper headlines that this disaster proved beyond doubt the urgent and immediate necessity for the dam. Members of the Congress felt at once a tremendous organized pressure upon them to implement their fourteen-year-old approval of the project with a building appropriation. Particularly intense was the pressure put on Representative Albert M. Cole, Republican representing Kansas' First District, in which the dam would be built. Theretofore he had opposed appropriations for the dam's construction, but he began now to waver.

The Kansas City *Star,* the Kansas City Chamber of Commerce, the flood-damaged interests of Topeka, the powerful lobbies for the Engineers, all these pressed for prompt action. In the Blue Valley, opponents of the dam were dazed by the disaster they themselves had suffered, but they rallied quickly nevertheless and were more tightly organized, more grim in their determination to "save the valley" than ever before. They were, it appeared, few against many; they were "little" people fighting "big" people; and they were seriously handicapped in their effort to gain popular support by the fact that they could offer at first no convincing counterproposals.

Of politically conservative Kansas no portion had been more solidly and consistently conservative than the Blue Valley. To most of them the MVA proposal was "socialistic" and hence of the devil; they had rejected it with vehemence, clinging instead to the belief, or at least the assertion, that "conservation" practices instituted by the "farmers themselves" with assistance from "technical experts" would "hold the water where it falls" and thus provide adequate flood control, or even actual prevention. Their public pronouncements to this effect had little persuasive power when balanced against the pronouncements of the Engineers (the latter were always well buttressed with statistics), and they were publicly contradicted by the U. S. Soil Conservation Service itself. The SCS was represented on the Inter-Agency Committee: it was as concerned as the next bureau with maintaining its identity against the "threat" of any valley-wide integration: and it hoped, like other Federal agencies, to profit from the disaster by receiving increased appropriations from the Congress. Bowing to the Engineers, SCS officials publicly agreed that only with big dams could such monster floods as that of '51 be controlled. They added, however, that a conservation program over the drainage area would increase the effectiveness and longevity of such dams; it would reduce the number and height of smaller floods as well as the rate of reservoir siltation. For these courtesies Army Engineer spokesmen reciprocated by saying that soil conservation was certainly a fine thing.

During the following months Tuttle Creek bid fair to become a national issue, recognized as such by millions of readers of popular magazines and the syndicated material in newspapers. No longer, at least as regards the dam, was there a vertebral sociological structure down the Blue. The people of the valley presented to the world a remarkably solid united front as they became aware that the 82nd Congress would probably decide their fate once and for all. They proved themselves to be increasingly adept at dramatizing their case. Their case itself became stronger as valley leaders educated themselves and their followers in the iniquities of the present bureaucratic tangle, the possibilities of playing one Federal agency against another, the meagerness of the physical data on which crucial decisions were taken, and the consequent "reasonable doubt" among many disinterested technical people that this dam—or indeed the Pick-Sloan "Big Dam" program in general—was the "best," much less the "only," way in which downstream flood protection could be achieved. They insisted with growing persuasive power that the Engineers went at flood control "wrong end to," attacking the problem *after* there had been a pile-up of waters, without sufficiently considering whether that pile-up could be prevented in the first place. The only answer the Engineers could make to the threat of recurrent floods downstream, cried valley spokesmen, was to create a permanent flood upstream. Surely there was a better way. Surely the logical place to begin flood-control planning was where the floods themselves began, with the rain as it fell upon the land. Only then could one sensibly design whatever downstream structures were needed, if any were, to prevent the inundation of cities.

In this the valley people felt themselves sustained by the technical achievements of the Soil Conservation Service, no matter how equivocal might be the public statements on this issue by SCS officials. Of particular value to them as propaganda ammunition was an article entitled "Big-Dam Foolishness" by Elmer T. Peterson, published in the *Country Gentleman* magazine for May 1952 and reprinted in *Reader's Digest* two months later. The article described Tuttle Creek as the focus of a bitter fight, of enormous significance, between big-dam and little-dam advocates. The "little dams" were SCS detention reservoirs of about 20 acres each, built on relatively infertile uplands (contrasting thus with big dams, which destroy the richest bottomland) and supplemented by such conservation farming methods as contour strip cropping, terracing, the grassing of waterways, the protection of steep slopes with permanent grass or timber, and "the assignment of each crop acre to the use for which it is best fitted" in terms of long-time erosion-resistant productivity. This type of flood control not only protects downstream areas more effectively than big dams can do, said Peterson; it also saves the soil from erosion, and the soil lost in such catastrophes as '51's flood is invaluable since it is irreplaceable.

The Peterson article gave a glowing account of the SCS's Washita Valley Agricultural Flood Control Project in Oklahoma, making a direct comparison between an earthen detention reservoir in the Mill Creek sub-watershed built by the SCS and the huge Denison reservoir (Lake Texoma) built by Army Engineers. The SCS's small upstream dam, wrote Peterson, would impound in its flood pool 5.22 inches of runoff from its drainage area, whereas the huge Denison reservoir downstream could impound only 1.31 inches of runoff "even if the pool were kept drained to its lowest point, which seldom happens, because water levels are held up for hydroelectric power and recreation." He cited the crucial test of the 4,000-acre Barnitz Creek sub-watershed when it was hit by a 100-year flood on May 16, 1951. Thirteen inches of rain fell within 24 hours, but Barnitz Creek "had been equipped with SCS detention reservoirs, farm ponds and other soil-conservation measures." The detention reservoirs absorbed 4 to 5 inches of runoff, said Peterson; the "drawdown"[2] and land-surface treatments did the rest. In consequence, Barnitz Creek did not go out of its banks, while neighboring creeks, receiving the same rain, went on a destructive rampage. Peterson also compared estimates by the SCS and the Army Engineers for

[2]This is an automatic outlet about halfway down the dam; when the impounded water reaches this level it flows through a pipe until the creek below is bankfull—then stops. There's a permanent pool below the drawdown which may be used for irrigation, whereas the upper part of the reservoir, behind the dam, is a flood pool—kept empty save when heavy rains come—making up 64 per cent of the structure's total capacity.

flood control on the Little Washita, a still-uncontrolled sub-watershed:

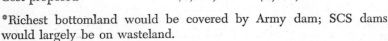

	ARMY PLAN	SCS PLAN[3]
Number of reservoirs	1	34
Drainage area, square miles	195	190
Flood storage, acre-feet	52,000	59,100
Permanent pool, acres (recreation)	1,950	2,100
Flood pool, acres	3,650	5,100
Bottoms inundated, acres	1,850*	1,600*
Bottomland protected	3,371	8,080
Cost proposed	$6,000,000	$1,983,000

*Richest bottomland would be covered by Army dam; SCS dams would largely be on wasteland.

All this made a profound impression in the Blue Valley. There had been organized for some time a Blue Valley Study Association, and under the chairmanship of Glenn Stockwell—a farmer who'd made a brilliant scholastic record at Kansas State College and who now demonstrated leadership qualities of a high order —the Blue Valley *did* study. It also acted. The two processes were fused in a manner that might have pleased John Dewey. Delegations were sent to Washington; carefully prepared statements were read into congressional records; letters by the score were written to newspapers; and many and various were the "publicity stunts" performed by sober-minded people who would normally shun such activities.

For a time it seemed that the congressional appropriation might again (and perhaps finally, this time) be prevented. Everything depended upon the Kansas delegation's standing firm upon the floor of the Congress. But Cole, as we have said, was wavering, and under the increasing pressures placed upon him he finally

[3]The fact that the scientific accuracy of this table was challenged by some SCS officials did not reduce its persuasiveness with the popular mind in the Blue Valley.

gave way altogether, switching from opposition to support of the Tuttle Creek Dam. He claimed that he still favored the watershed approach so vociferously pressed upon him by his Blue Valley constituents but that the alternatives now presented to him were between *some* flood control and none: he felt in duty bound to choose the former. Thus, late in the session, the Engineers got what they wanted—a $5,000,000 appropriation to begin construction of a dam whose estimated total cost was $87,000,000 and whose actual cost might be in the neighborhood of $160,-000,000 if past Engineer performances proved an accurate guide. The Engineers lost no time in their eagerness to present a *fait accompli* to a still-doubtful public. Dozens of men were soon scurrying over valley fields, making test borings and surveys; bids were promptly advertised for; in early September the contract for preliminary construction was let; and in October actual work began.

A wave of bitterness swept over the valley; passions grew dangerously large as the Engineers seemed to be winning their object despite everything valley people could do. There is a richness of the spirit that can be developed only through generations of life upon the same soil, in the same landscape. Rural people are more inclined to feel this deeply than urban people are. They know that there are uses as well as beauties in a past which lives through the present toward a future that will be continuous with it. Often this is what distinguishes them most sharply from completely urbanized Americans, whose operations are likely to appear nervously tense and jerky to rural eyes and whose natures are likely to seem brittle, shallow, untruthful, and (under a smooth surface sophistication) childishly avid of sensual pleasures which blunt aesthetic and moral perceptions. Dangerous stereotypes come into play when the issue becomes one of city vs. country. The city man sees his opponent as a country yokel as slow of wit as he is of speech, ignorant of all that lies beyond a near horizon, and forever inclined to brand as "immoral" or even "atheistic" whatever practical proposal fails to accord with what he believes to be his own economic interest. The rural man sees his opponent as a city slicker incapable of the finer emotions, grossly materialistic, and as false as he is glib in the service of a purely selfish desire. The friction of such stereotypes sparks an inhumanity—and there was friction of precisely this nature in the Blue Valley in '52. In the expressions on valley people's faces, in the things they said and the gestures they made as they said them, was a covert violence which could easily, one felt, explode into inhuman acts. Why, they wanted to know, should they acquiesce in their sacrifice to the industrial interests of Kansas City? Why should they treat the Army Engineer employees as other than contemptible lackeys of the coarse fat boys down the river? If they could not get at the fat boys directly, they might strike through the lackeys.

"This is a fight to the finish, and it may become violent," wrote Richard Kleiner, NEA staff correspondent after a visit to the valley in August of '52. "The Engineers, now surveying the area, stay in a tourist hotel in Randolph, and they don't go out alone. . . . They may be kidding, but there's a deadly ring to their voices when the Blue Valley men talk about what they'd like to do.

" 'I've had the dangedest urge,' said one man, 'to throw a match into that field of straw where the drill rigs are. It's dry as dust and would burn right nice.'

" 'Another good deal,' said a young farmer, 'would be to take a high-powered rifle and shoot them engines on them rigs.' "

It was fortunate that common-sensical valley leadership, however disgusted it became, would steadily discourage such futile aggressions. . . .

A strictly neutral observer, then, might see reason overbalanced by passion throughout the whole period of the struggle. To him it might appear that if the Engineers were driven by a "passion" to Build a Big Dam, the people of the valley were driven by an equivalent "passion" to keep them from doing it. On these grounds there might seem to be little choice between the two.

Nevertheless, our strictly neutral observer would, I think, have been himself inclined to oppose the building of the dam in '52—unless he were one of those who are insensitive to the lyric values of tradition and enamored of change for change's sake. Prudence and our natural indolence alike proclaim that the burden of proof in such issues as this rests upon those who would radically modify long-established institutions, customs, and ways of life: it is up to them to prove that the drastic change they propose is definitely superior to all possible, less drastic alternatives, and that the evils consequent upon their act are definitely smaller than the evils which are otherwise inevitable.

Surely the change here proposed was drastic enough as far as the valley was concerned; surely the valley was to be pitied, even by those to whom her death seemed a justifiable price for downstream security. Tuttle Creek Dam, according to the most recent published design (it was difficult to keep up with the changes in it), would create a reservoir of some 50,000 acres, impounding 2,280,000 acre-feet of water at high-pool stage. It would destroy the present homes of some 4,000 people who, however liberally they were paid for their property, must feel torn up by the very roots of their lives. Nine villages, most of them tiny but all of them among the oldest in Kansas, lay in the area to be permanently flooded. Several cemeteries lay there, and some of the most productive cropland in the Middle West. No truly sensitive man could stand in the churchyard at Mariadahl that year without suffering sharp pangs of regret for the shortening term of this rare community, and he must feel a species of angry despair if he believed that the necessity to bury all this under silt-laden waters had by no means been proved.

Despair, however, was not permitted to dominate the valley's mood. The people of the valley did not admit defeat, even when construction was under way: they fought on, harder than before and with better organization. Blue Valley women descended in intimidating fashion upon the Republican presidential candidate in Denver, and upon President Truman, too, when he visited Kansas City, and they saw to it that the events were nationally publicized. There blossomed in the front yards of houses and along the main highways signs proclaiming Tuttle Creek to be "Big-Dam Foolishness" (à la the afore-mentioned article by Elmer Peterson), and photographs of these appeared in the press. The governor of Kansas was prevailed upon to conduct, with state executive funds and through disinterested professional people, a survey of the flood problem and its solution in the Kansas Basin, supplementing data already gathered at considerable expense by the Santa Fe Railroad. State legislators were involved in preparation of a law whose passage would permit the formation of legal "watershed" units, with certain regulatory powers, capable of co-operating with individuals and groups and governmental bodies in establishing the "wise land-use," the farm ponds, the detention reservoirs, and the other possible means of halting floods before they have well begun.

But as it turned out the most important move was the decision of Glenn Stockwell and other valley leaders to organize politically to defeat Representative Cole in the November elections. This decision was made against the inertia of nearly a century of monolithic Republicanism in Kansas' First District: it meant active, campaigning support of the Democratic candidate, a 73-year-old farmer from Hiawatha named Howard S. Miller—a man who had run unsuccessfully in 1936 as a strong New Dealer—and there were many in the valley who had been taught since early childhood to look upon a Democrat as, by definition, a rascal. Never in all its history had the First District elected a Democrat. Only with great difficulty had the party persuaded Miller to run, to "fill out the ticket," and he confessed himself to be persuaded, at last, only because the campaign would enable him to do educational work on behalf of soil conservation, to which he had long been committed. (He had been one of the first farmers in his county to co-operate with the SCS in a complete-farm erosion-control program on his 800-acre farm, and he had been elected president of the local conservation-promoting Walnut Creek Watershed Association.) To him as to Stockwell and other Blue Valley leaders it might well have appeared that he had no slightest chance of election. Cole had won his seat for the fourth time in 1950 with a majority of over 30,000; he had earned a seniority whose value in terms of congressional power was widely recognized among his constituents; he would have the support of the Kansas City *Star* and nearly all the papers published in his district; and he should be able to pile up huge majorities in such downstream urban centers as Topeka, which had suffered terribly in the '51 flood and was presumed to favor Tuttle Creek as fervently as the Blue Valley opposed it. Add to all this the fact that the presidential candidate, Dwight Eisenhower, was Kansas' "favorite son," a man of such overwhelming popularity that he seemed capable of pulling into office with him the entire state Republican ticket—add this, and the situation from Miller's point of view appeared hopeless.

What followed, therefore, was an amazing demonstration of grass-roots democracy.

Beginning in early October, the Blue Valley group conducted an intensive campaign on Miller's behalf. A working alliance was formed with the state CIO, which, having studied the Blue Valley situation and conferred with Miller, came out against Tuttle Creek; they would in any case have opposed Cole, whose voting record was "reactionary" from the CIO point of view. This alliance was of strategic importance, since the CIO, actively working on Miller's behalf, might whittle down Cole's Topeka majority. More decisive was the work of the women of the valley. They toured the district in caravans behind a sound truck plastered with signs saying "Republicans for Miller" and "Stop Big-Dam Foolishness"; they passed out Miller cards by the thousand and helped organize public meetings. Stockwell and his colleagues saw to it that all these events were well publicized. Miller himself, in public speeches and radio talks and articles for the newspapers, attacked Tuttle Creek repeatedly as a "symptom of bureaucracy gone mad" and pledged his support to the Hoover Commission recommendations which would "strip the Army Engineers of their arrogant power."

Thus did Tuttle Creek become the issue between Cole and Miller—the only popular issue—and on that issue, to the utter amazement of professional politicians, Miller won by a 7,000 majority. He was the only Kansas Democrat to win any office of importance that year.

The event seemed to have far more than local significance, particularly in view of the narrowness of the Republican majority in the House. In the immediate aftermath it appeared that the Tuttle Creek project—which the Engineers themselves had insisted was of crucial importance to the entire Pick-Sloan scheme —might be at least temporarily halted, that the Engineers had suffered a severe body blow. Many thought that with Miller's victory the country had won another chance to put into effect the water policy whose outlines had been made clear by the Hoover Commission and every other disinterested body that had studied the problem. There might even be a chance that the policy could be effectuated through the establishment of a Missouri Valley Authority—for this administrative arrangement was less firmly resisted by the most influential leaders of the Blue Valley as they saw with increasing clarity what seemed to them the deficiencies in alternative proposals.[4]

5

Some Alternative Proposals   Between 1944 and 1952 no less than five bills to establish a Missouri Valley Authority had been introduced to the Senate by Senator James E. Murray, Montana Democrat. Each of the last four was a modification of its predecessor, designed to remove some of the objections that had been raised—and each languished and died, having been bitterly opposed by the National Rivers and Harbors Congress, the U. S. Chamber of Commerce, private electric utilities, who joined one another in national advertising campaigns, the Associated General Contractors, the Kansas City *Star,* and numerous similar organs and pressure groups of conservative bent. Virtually every newspaper in the Kansas Basin was extremely conservative; on nearly all of them the publisher's bias rather than objective news values determined how controversial stories were presented in news columns; and in almost none of them[1] was the MVA proposal presented to readers in a manner that seemed fair to MVA supporters. Instead the proposal was so maligned as "socialistic" and "dictatorial" that the very mention of it stopped the processes of reason while stirring those of prejudice all up and down the basin. Not until the Army Engineers gained their triumph at Tuttle Creek did residents of the Blue Valley, for example, begin to wonder if an MVA wouldn't be more responsive to their inter-

[4]This glow of optimism faded a good deal between November of '52 and January 20, '53. The budget proposed for the Federal government by President Truman in early January contained, despite Miller's protests, an item of some $15,000,000 to continue construction of the Tuttle Creek Dam during the next fiscal year.

[1]A notable exception was the Manhattan, Kansas, *Daily Tribune,* which supported MVA.

ests and ideas than the Engineers will ever be. It could hardly be less so.

Like TVA, the proposed MVA would be a Federal corporation.[2] A board of five directors would be appointed by the President, at least three of whom must have been residents of the basin for at least five years. They would employ a general manager. Headquarters of the corporation would be in the valley, and its first duty would be to prepare that comprehensive plan for regional development whose desperate need has for so long been evident. The plan must be approved by the Congress before appropriations are made to carry it out, and before it is presented to the Congress it must be approved by an advisory board comprising twelve citizens representing agricultural, commercial and industrial, labor, and wildlife and recreation interests; the governors of the ten Missouri Basin states; and the principal officer of each of the Federal Departments of Agriculture, Interior, Commerce, Justice, Army, and Labor, and of the Federal Power Commission and the board of governors of the Federal Reserve Bank. The state governors would also constitute a special advisory committee on Federal-state relations.

The bill was carefully drawn to protect the state's interests in their watersheds and to protect their water rights. For instance, it would preserve the amendment to the Flood Control Act of 1944 whereby the upper basin would be given prior claim to the use of water for irrigation and other consumptive purposes, and in the allowance of water for irrigation purposes one aim would be to preserve the family-sized farm. The bill "recognizes the existence of an important body of law affecting the public lands, irrigation, reclamation, grazing, geological survey, national parks and monuments, mines and mineral holdings, and

[2]The author is indebted to Richard G. Baumhoff, author of *The Dammed Missouri Valley* (Knopf, 1951), for the digest of the 1949 bill's provisions.

forest land that must not be affected in any manner." Electric power could be sold by the Authority only at wholesale, except where farms and rural communities are "not adequately served by existing utilities at reasonable rates"; to these, retail sales could be made—and it was of course this provision, which raised the question of what constitutes "reasonable rates," that private electric companies most violently objected to. All MVA profits would go into the Federal treasury, which meant that all funds for MVA operations and construction would have to be appropriated by the Congress. The Authority would make payments to state and local governments in lieu of taxes on its holdings, and it was anticipated that tax revenues of these governments would actually increase as MVA improvements boosted values.

The bill also sought to prevent usurpation or duplication by MVA of efforts which might as well or better be made by existing Federal agencies. MVA could, for example, enter into contracts with the Army Engineers, the Bureau of Reclamation, and the Department of Agriculture, all of which might handle the same general assignments as had formerly been theirs, though in accordance (for the first time) with a truly integrated, comprehensive valley plan. Projects for which authorizations and appropriations had already been provided could not be delayed or dropped but must be incorporated into the initial MVA plan. To some observers it seemed apparent that this last provision was weakening opposition to an MVA in proportion as more and more projects of the Pick-Sloan Plan were actually achieved. Thus the Kansas City *Star*, rabidly opposed to the MVA proposal in the mid-1940s, had relatively kind things to say in the early 1950s. Meanwhile MVA supporters were unhappy about the probability that an MVA, if created, would be presented with a *fait accompli* and thus deprived of the major value to be achieved from it— though even then an MVA seemed to them preferable to the bureaucratic chaos existing behind the false front of Inter-Agency.

Much more carefully drawn than its predecessors, this bill of 1949 did not, however, reduce the opposition to it by such pressure groups as the Mississippi Valley Association. That association's *Mississippi Valley Newsletter* for March 1949 asserted that the "new bill goes far beyond the provisions proposed in the previous MVA measures," that the "new powers sought would establish precedents which would profoundly affect the form of government under which this country has prospered for nearly two centuries," and that the "broad grants of authority . . . [would] exceed the powers given the Tennessee Valley Authority." The *Newsletter* went on: "The bill, for example, confers upon the Authority to be created broad powers of eminent domain. . . . It can be logically construed . . . that the Authority has the legal right to condemn and sell any land or property in the Missouri Basin on the sole ground that the profits would be used in furtherance of its plans. . . . If adopted, the Murray bill would establish the precedent that the Federal government should nationalize the electric power industry. . . . In at least 27 instances the grants of power are limited only by the phrase as the Authority 'deems necessary.' "

More disinterested and hence persuasive with intelligent people were objections raised by the Hoover Commission's Task Force on Natural Resources to any further extension of the valley authority type of organization. The Task Force sought carefully to evaluate the TVA, though hampered by the fact that there was as yet no comprehensive study of its "experience." On the whole, they found TVA good for its area and invaluable as an experiment in regional development, demonstrating the immense advantages to be gained from dealing with a river basin as a unit rather than a loose collection of purposes, problems, and geographic areas. They recognized the values of flexibility and of decentralized Federal activity; they strongly recommended the continuance of TVA itself along the lines already laid down. But they questioned "the extent to which TVA's experience is a safe guide for predicting the way in which similar organizations would work in other areas." They pointed out that development problems along the Tennessee were unusually complex and closely interrelated, requiring perhaps a broader grant of legislative authority to TVA "than may be required for Federal agencies operating in basins having less difficult problems." In general, they seemed to fear that a wide imitation of TVA in other areas might dangerously complicate the organization and procedures of government and might substitute for the present evils of too much centralization the equal evils of too great a decentralization. They spoke of the possibilities of sectional rivalries, of a friction of Authorities, which would result in a neglect of "over-riding *national*[3] interests in the development of our water and other resources." They therefore recommended that Federal resource-development functions be entrusted to regular departments of the government, "provided drastic reorganizations [of these] are effected." Among the "important values in the traditional vertical bureau and departmental type of organization" were listed the following:

a. It provides greater assurance of similar treatment of similar resource problems throughout the Nation than would a regional type of organization.
b. It makes possible the utilization of central services which cannot be afforded in each regional area.
c. It makes possible the development of standards by which similar programs in many river basins can be measured.
d. It operates as a restraint on sectional tendencies which might influence a regional authority to develop resources in a manner detrimental to the best national interests.

It must be reiterated, however, that these values outweighed those of the Authority device, in the Task Force's mind, *only* if

[3]Italics mine.

"drastic reorganizations" of the present Federal departmental structure were made. The Task Force recommended the abolition of the Department of Interior and its replacement, in part, by a new Department of Natural Resources.[4] Within this new department would be a consolidated Water Development Service to administer, among other things, the present functions of the Bureau of Reclamation, the river-development functions of the Engineers, and the power-marketing functions of the present Interior's Division of Power; and a consolidated Forest and Range Service, based upon the present Forest Service (now in the Department of Agriculture) and including forest- and range-management functions now carried on through Interior's Bureau of Land Management. "Activities dealing with harvest crops and domestic livestock on farms should continue to be handled by the Department of Agriculture," said a footnote to the report—and these activities included the erosion-control work of the Soil Conservation Service. The Water Development and Forest and Range Services would be "decentralized" into regions, each region coinciding "where practicable" with river basins "to facilitate 'grass roots' decisions, inter-service co-operation and local participation in planning." Further, "regional advisory committees should be set up for both Services to give full representation to state and local interests and to other Federal agencies substantially concerned."

The proposal, however, did not gain the approval of a majority of the twelve-member Hoover Commission, which instead favored a reorganization and enlargement of the Department of Interior whereby it would "be given more clearly the mission of develop-

[4]Another Task Force, that on Public Works, recommended a Department of Works which would assume many of the same functions as Natural Resources. Both proposals had, as primary motives, elimination of the friction between the Engineers and the Bureau of Reclamation.

ment of subsoil and water resources." "As these activities require large public works," the Commission report continued, "we recommend that other major public works also be managed by this Department." Three bureaus now in the department would be transferred elsewhere, but to it would be transferred: "a. Flood Control and Rivers and Harbors improvement from the Department of the Army. b. Public Building Construction from the Federal Works Agency. c. Community Services from the Federal Works Agency. d. Certain major construction to be assigned on behalf of other agencies of the Government, except where carried on by grants-in-aid programs." As anticipated, recommendation a., above, aroused fervent opposition from the Army Engineers and their powerful friends, while on the Commission itself were two able spokesmen for Engineers' interests: Senator John L. McClellan of Arkansas who, as we've seen, was president of the Rivers and Harbors Congress, and Carter Manasco, formerly representative from Alabama. These two filed a strong dissenting report in which they argued that stripping the Army Engineers of civil functions "would be a crippling blow to our National Defense Establishment," since the performance of these functions was of "immeasurable value . . . in better equipping [Corps of Engineers'] personnel for wartime service."[5]

It was in view of the difficulty of obtaining favorable congressional action on the Hoover recommendations that the President's

[5]This argument had been anticipated by the Task Force on Public Works which, in its report, said that "less than 200 Army Engineers are involved [in rivers and harbors work] and . . . the remainder of the personnel under their control . . . are civilians who supply most of the detailed knowledge and continuing direction. If the Army Engineers supply unusual ability and obtain invaluable training by contact with this responsibility, there is no reason why the same and even better results cannot be obtained by assigning them and corresponding officers of the Navy and Air Forces, on a proper, dignified, and respected basis, to a central consolidated Works Department."

Water Resources Policy Commission in 1950[6] proposed (a) that a separate river-basin commission be set up for each of the major basins and (b) that a Federal Board of Review be established to pass on all development-project suggestions.

Chaired by Morris L. Cooke, who had long pressed for a practical conception of our natural resources as a "seamless web" of soil and water and forests, etc., the Commission was emphatic in its criticism of present bureaucratic arrangements whereby Federal agencies compete rather than co-operate with one another; it emphasized the need for a "set of clearly defined national objectives established by Congress" to which all Federal agencies "should be directed" to conform. "These objectives, as outlined in detail by this Commission, should reflect the general purpose of water resources investment to achieve the maximum sustained use of lakes, rivers, and their associated land and ground water resources, to support a continuing high level of prosperity throughout the country," said the Commission's report. "They should include the safeguarding of our resources against deterioration from floods; the improvement and higher utilization of these resources to support an expanding economy and national security; assistance to regional development; expansion of all types of recreational opportunity to meet increasing needs; protection of public health; and opportunity for greater use of transportation and electric power. . . . Congress should direct the responsible Federal agencies to submit new proposals for water resources development to Congress only in the form of basin programs which deal with entire basins as units and which take into account all relevant purposes in water and land development." The Commission also said that "Congress should direct the . . . agencies to co-operate with one another and with the appropriate state agencies in the necessary surveys and plans."

[6] *A Water Policy for the American People,* Vol. I of Report of President's Water Resources Policy Commission.

The Commission was well aware, however, that what *ought* to be, as regards co-ordination, could never be achieved without administrative rearrangements; "lacking such agency reorganization as was recommended by the Commission on Organization of the Executive Branch of the Government [Hoover Commission]," it urged the Congress to establish the separate river-basin commissions heretofore mentioned. "These commissions, set up on a representative basis, should be authorized to coordinate the surveys, construction activities, and operations of the Federal agencies in the several basins, under the guidance of independent chairmen appointed by the President and with the participation of State agencies in the planning process. . . . Congress should designate the Federal departments and independent agencies to participate in the river basin commissions." The project proposals emerging from these activities would be passed upon by the recommended Federal Board of Review.

This report was issued in December 1950. A few months earlier —in June of the same year—a report of some 200 mimeographed pages was issued by the Engineers' Joint Council's Water Policy Panel. Panel and Commission pretty well agreed as to the objectives of a sound national water policy; they differed somewhat as to method, the Panel favoring a more "decentralized" approach to the problem than did the Commission. The Panel said that "that which can be done by the individual should be done by him, and that which requires collective action should be done at the lowest governmental level practicable"—a general statement with which, perhaps, most of the Commission members would agree "in principle" but whose application might reveal considerable differences in attitude. One observer[7] has compared the differences between the Panel and Commission approaches to

[7] F. D. Farrell, president emeritus, Kansas State College, address entitled "Toward a National Water Policy" before a Forum on Flood Control at K.S.C., November 27 and 28, 1951.

those between Jefferson and Hamilton on the form of Federal government, "the Commission tending to be Hamiltonian, the Panel Jeffersonian." This observer made the suggestive remark that "the outcome of the Hamilton-Jefferson controversy was a series of compromises which, upon the whole, have worked fairly well for more than 150 years."

More limited in its scope than the administrative proposals discussed above was the suggestion embodied in the Miami Conservancy District, a suggestion much discussed in the Kansas Basin after the 1951 flood.

The district idea was concerned exclusively with flood prevention. It was the response made by the people of the 4,000-square-mile Miami Valley in southwestern Ohio to a disastrous flood in March 1913, during which 225 lives were lost and an estimated $80,000,000 of damages incurred. In the immediate aftermath of that disaster, the stricken towns of the 4,000-square-mile valley established committees with a view to solving their flood-control problems individually. Of course they quickly found that the problem must be approached on a watershed basis, whereupon the committees co-operated to form a Miami Valley Flood Prevention Association and employed A. E. Morgan (later a director of the Tennessee Valley Authority) and his Morgan Engineering Company of Memphis, Tennessee, to report on flood-prevention plans. Some $2,000,000 was raised by subscription in the valley to finance the preliminary work, and from this sum were paid the costs of engineering surveys, of legal assistance in drafting the Conservancy Act of Ohio, of planning engineering works, and of defending the district against suits as work proceeded.

The Ohio Conservancy Law, enacted as a result of Miami Valley planning, permitted the establishment of a conservancy district through which plans could be made, contracts let for flood prevention, and costs assessed against the property that had been damaged by previous floods and would be protected from future ones—though the cost assessments must never be greater than the benefits derived. The Miami District, between 1914 and 1918, built five reservoir dams at a cost of $33,000,000 —all of them assessed to the property benefited—and supplemented these with channel improvement through the cities. This work prevented any recurrence of such disasters as 1913's. In 1937, for example, storms in the Miami Valley were more severe than those of 1913, yet there was no loss of life and no property damage in the areas which in 1913 were almost ruined.

The effectiveness of these reservoirs, the manner of their financing, and the fact that the dams were "dry"—storing water only during periods of flood-producing rains and permitting the reservoir area to be used for agriculture in other periods—all impressed strongly the people of the Blue Valley and other portions of the Kansas Basin threatened by permanent inundation behind Army Engineer structures. If big dams must be built for flood prevention, said many people, the "dry" dams were clearly preferable to "wet" ones. Other people, however, stressed the presumed advantages of multiple-purpose reservoirs whereby a much more favorable ratio of costs to benefits might be achieved —and there were increasing numbers who, as we've seen, opposed "Big-Dam Foolishness" altogether as an "outmoded" approach to flood control.

Finally must be added to the conservancy-district idea the idea of flood-plain zoning whereby the state or its political subdivisions under the police power would zone flood plains and prescribe the uses to which they could be put. One kind of legalistic thinking behind this idea was well expressed by John G. Stutz, executive director of the League of Kansas Municipalities, in a speech before the Forum on Flood Control held at Kansas State College in November 1951. "It is assumed . . . that any flood plain [i.e., the area of a stream basin which has been built with flood water] is a flood-threatened area and anyone who occupies a flood plain takes a calculated risk on a flood," said Stutz. "This calculated risk, however, is so vast and so irregular that it has been nearly impossible to develop any economical plan of flood insurance. Every stream, however, has a clear water right, flood water right to all of its flood plain. Those who take title to land in a flood plain do so subject to prior rights, titles and easements of the streams which built such land. All persons should know that sooner or later the stream will claim the use of its flood plain lands for carrying flood water and for the storage of flood water silts. It is reported by Dr. Walter T. Kollmorgan, chairman of the Department of Geography of the University of Kansas, that these principles were recognized some 250 years ago when the king of France made it clear to the people who settled in the lower Mississippi that 'the grantee would build levees at his own expense and that whatever property loss he suffered from floods was a servitude to his grant.'"

Kansas in 1952 had no statute on flood-plain zoning, though several precedents for such legislation were on the books. Stutz cited the state water-appropriation act, which prohibits the taking of water from streams except for domestic purposes; the "general rule" that a person may not change or divert the channel of a stream on his land to the injury of another landowner; and Article 20, Chapter 2, of Kansas' General Statutes of 1949, whereby the state makes it the duty of the owner of lands "to plant perennial grasses, shrubs, or trees or annual or biennial crops and by cultivation at proper times and in proper manner to prevent or minimize wind powered erosion of the soil and dust blowing therefrom on his downwind neighbors." The law provides that if a landowner fails to take adequate steps to prevent dust blowing, it is the duty of the county commissioners to take such steps; if the commissioners do so, the cost may be assessed against the landowner, becoming a tax lien against his land. Stutz strongly recommended that Kansas enact a law authorizing flood-plain zoning "as a basic means of public protection service." He also recommended "the consideration of a basic law by which a landowner is charged with a measure of responsibility for the volume of runoff water from his land and the silts contained therein in much the same manner as the Kansas State law" dealing with dust blowing.

Of course the flood-plain-zoning idea was not deemed, of itself alone, a sufficient answer to the flood problem, but it was one device among the many which, tied together in a co-ordinated program, might accomplish the desired end. As such it was recognized by the President's Water Resources Policy Commission.

Said the Commission report:

There are three general applications of flood plain zoning:
1. Prohibition of encroachment upon an established floodway to insure that the capacity of the floodway is not reduced by obstructions and to prevent or minimize future flood damage in the unprotected area of the floodway.
2. Restrictions on development in the protected or unprotected flood plain areas where maintenance of the flow capacity is not a controlling consideration. The purpose here is to prevent or minimize future flood damage, particularly landward of levees which provide only partial protection, or to eliminate works which provide full or partial protection.
3. Restriction of developments in areas subject to inundation by impounded water in connection with reservoirs or sumps necessary for the proper functioning of interior drainage facilities landward of levees.

The Commission concluded that "such flood plain zoning might, in the long run, save many lives and much property, for, in spite of all flood control works, the future always holds the possibility of unusual floods for which the maximum of protection would prove inadequate." Such zoning should therefore be encouraged.

Of Education and the River

A Hole in the Ground; a College on the Hill **1**

Example: Our Response to the Crisis of '51 **2**

The Organic Concept as a Guide to Curricular Changes **3**

1

A Hole in the Ground; a College on the Hill   By February of 1953 a giant hole had been dug beside Kansas Highway 13, five miles north of Manhattan. From that hole came the earth which, dumped into the Blue three quarters of a mile to the east, would divert that river to a new channel while the permanent Tuttle Creek Dam was built. Men with bulldozers, men with trucks, men with giant shovels and cranes had already ruined this portion of the valley; they worked on a twenty-four-hour-a-day schedule, driven (as all who watched suspected) by a powerful bureau's determination to have its own way regardless of the tide of popular opinion which seemed now to flow against it. Each shovelful of earth dumped into the river was, from that bureau's point of view, a hostage against the people's will, and the great hole in the ground might, by that bureau, be deemed a "last ditch" in which all who favored the present methods of river development must firmly stand.

By that time, as we've seen, Tuttle Creek was firmly established as a national symbol. The election of Congressman Miller on an anti-Tuttle Creek platform, the publicity given the Blue Valley's fight for life, the Army Engineers' reiteration that Tuttle Creek was a key structure in the entire Pick-Sloan Plan, the heightened realization that the halting of Tuttle Creek must therefore mean a new approach to river development in the Missouri Valley if not over the country as a whole—all these made the symbol important. They gave to the sight of those scurrying, muddy men, deep in the ditch they had dug, a significant excitement.

In that same mild bright February there stood upon a hill, six miles to the southwest, the limestone buildings of a college. Between the hill and the great hole beside Highway 13 was a definite connection in the eyes of at least one observer. For one thing, some of the policy-making personnel of those Federal agencies and private corporations most directly concerned with river development were alumni of Kansas State College of Agriculture and Applied Science. The practical actions of these men might measure with some accuracy the kind of education they had received. If there was chaos in the college's curricula, if the institution lacked clearly defined over-all educational aims, that fact might be partially expressed in the chaos of bureaucracy and competing selfishnesses whose symbol, for many, was the Tuttle Creek Dam. But for me the connection was deeper and wider than this, the college being as much a national symbol as the dam. Kansas State is no unique phenomenon on the American scene. Rather is it typical of major educational trends, its triumphs and failures and general nature being duplicated in scores of other institutions across the land. Since this is so, Kansas State might provide a laboratory in which to examine the question of *why* the American mind has been so incompetent, apparently, to deal comprehensively with river problems.

To this examination I wish to devote the closing pages of my own effort to learn how to think about a river, beginning where Kansas State itself began and reviewing briefly the ideological history of the institution.

The college was organized in 1863, a few months after Abraham Lincoln signed the Morrill Land Grant Act, by whose terms 90,000 acres of Federal land were granted as an endowment to a state institution which would "promote the liberal and practical education of the industrial classes." Kansas State was conceived, then, as a "people's" institution in conscious "democratic" revolt against earlier conceptions of higher education—and as it developed in this tradition it neglected the "liberal" while emphasizing the "practical" aims of its work.

When we Americans founded our first colleges upon the Eastern seaboard we patterned them, naturally, after European universities, particularly those of England. This meant that we began American higher education in what was essentially an aristocratic tradition—a cultural vestige of the feudal order which no longer prevailed, or was rapidly ceasing to prevail, in politics and economics. College education was then conceived to be the virtually exclusive prerogative of the "higher classes." As a privilege of aristocracy, it was denied to common folk, who must, with few exceptions, be content with the equivalent of our grade or high school education. And "gentlemen" went to college in those days not only to acquire the kind of classical erudition which would serve as the badge of their class distinction but also to achieve a cultural development which would enable them to govern themselves and their "inferiors." By this view, a gentleman was primarily concerned with Truth, especially in its "higher manifestations," as he pursued his education, whereas the lower orders were concerned chiefly with "mere" utility. The implication was that Truth and Utility were distinct and separate from one another. Hence college curricula placed great emphasis on Greek and Latin, on philosophy and the arts, and gave little emphasis to vocational preparation. Indeed, almost the only vocations for which specific preparation was provided by colleges were the "gentlemanly" professions of law, the ministry, and medicine. Naturally the kind of men produced by such colleges were ill suited to many of the crucial needs of an expanding pioneering economy, and particularly were they ill suited to the Western frontier. They were too often "impractical" in the literal meaning of that word. They even had—many of them —a contempt for "practicality," deeming the word a synonym for "servility."

Against this conception of education and its end products, the land-grant-college movement proclaimed the dignity of physical labor, the superior virtue of experimental science over classical scholarship, and the right of "agriculture and the mechanic arts" (as courses) to the prestige theretofore accorded Greek, Latin, philosophy, and the humanities in general. The early administrators of the land-grant colleges often went farther than this: often they rejected the classics and humanities altogether, replacing them in the curriculum with courses in telegraphy, woodworking, printing, and practical farming. This happened at Kansas State College in the 1870s. Only gradually was it realized that the "how" of agriculture, engineering, business, and industry required at least some grasp of the "why"—that is, of the theory which generalized prevailing practice or from which prevailing practice was derived. Courses in basic sciences were then strengthened, and there were restored to the curriculum some of the courses in history, literature, and languages that had been earlier removed. In the 1890s, when the Populist revolt swept across the Kansas plains, courses in economics and political science, whose aim was to indoctrinate, became the controversial centers of the curriculum —but this was a transient furor and did little to modify the fact that Kansas State, as a representative land-grant institution, emphasized vocational and professional training virtually to the exclusion of "liberal" education as the author of the land-grant act would have defined it. Indeed, the typical faculty member came to regard training and education as the same thing, which is to say that, as a theoretical assumption, the distinction between "living" and "making a living" was broken down.

This latter assumption was given intellectual dignity in the late nineteenth and early twentieth centuries by the rise of pragmatism, or instrumentalism—a point of view which came to dominate the American system of education almost as completely as Aristotelianism had dominated the schools of medieval Europe. The new philosophy said in effect that Truth and Utility, far from being opposed to one another, are actually identical. An idea is true, said the pragmatist, if it "works" successfully in the problem-situation which stimulated its formation; its truth, then, *is* its problem-solving efficacy. Truth, said John Dewey, is adverbial; the word "true" properly modifies verbs rather than nouns, and under no circumstances are we to assume that there is in actual existence a Universal Truth of which all particular truths are aspects or manifestations. Thus pragmatism revealed itself as the antithesis of systematic philosophy, impatient of those restraints on impulse and action which are inevitably imposed by a rigorous logic with its concern for a total consistency. Pragmatism perfectly rationalized the restless, expansive, energetic mood of America, giving intellectual weapons into the hands of those who would defend that mood against penetrating criticisms by philosophic idealists. From the standpoint of our present essay, it had the great value of conceiving the world as actively developing rather than passively existing; it therefore knocked down many useless fences which had inhibited progress across the fields of knowledge. Moreover, the fervor with which it was proclaimed by its proponents was sufficient by itself to thaw into new life many minds that had been frozen stiffly into classical molds. Undoubtedly a greater freedom and flexibility was given American thought.

These are considerable virtues. They were not, however, unaccompanied by vices—and the vices were nowhere more visible nor more unfortunate than in the educational movement, which, though already under way when pragmatism was born, was further stimulated and distinctively shaped by pragmatic theory.

In his definition of truth as efficacy, the pragmatist fed that power-madness which, as Bertrand Russell has remarked, is the greatest social danger of our age. For notice how easily the definition leads to a "might-makes-right" ethical standard! The idea which "works" in the immediate problem-situation is the idea which prevails; prevalence over opposing ideas in a specific situation may therefore be taken as a test of truth; and since prevalence may be the result of coercive force, force rather than intelligence may be deemed the *ultimate* determinant of a concept's validity. This anti-intellectualism is reinforced by the pragmatist's fervent denial of "radical finalism" and of all concepts of eternal, general truth. The denial not only leads toward that contempt for speculative thought ("mere" theorizing, "mere" abstraction) which is now so typically American, but also prevents any genuine organization of knowledge, since it is only in terms of general principle, regarded as a common denominator of ideas, that the many and various "truths" discovered by experience can be realized as a coherent whole. In the absence of unifying principle, classification replaces organization: ideas and items of information have no internal relation to one another but remain in all respects distinct and separate, like marbles of precisely limited meaning placed in some box of category designed for purposes of convenience.

Of the general effects of this upon such typically American

schools as Kansas State, and through them upon river development, three things may be said:

First, in the absence of unifying principle, vocational interests determined curricula, and since technology breeds vocational specialization, the curricula multiplied endlessly. The breadth of subject matter in each of them was reduced almost proportionately. In recent literature designed to attract high school graduates, Kansas State bragged that it could now train its students in more than 200 different specialties, and there were few who saw that this might indicate an appalling fragmentation of mind, an appalling shrinkage of the student's general knowledge, an appalling neglect of the *whole* person, whose development ought to be education's purpose in a free society. It was not surprising that the graduates of such institutions demonstrated, as I believe, a remarkable incapacity to deal adequately with over-all problems of river development. On each segment of those problems we Americans could focus enormous specialized technical skill, but we generally failed even to attempt to see those problems as wholes. Moreover, we displayed truly amazing capacities for self-deception as we shaped out opinions on such matters as the Tuttle Creek Dam, easily assigning high moral purposes to proposals which would serve our private economic interest, though perhaps at great cost in terms of the general welfare.

Second, and closely related to the above, the sense of intellectual community which prevailed when students took most of their courses in common and shared their insights and mental enthusiasms with one another was much weakened where it was not actually destroyed; here again we find organism denied in favor of piecemeal, essentially mechanical developments. The principles which organize knowledge are the bases for communication. They provide the common ground on which men of diverse practical interests and backgrounds may stand together. And when they are denied, the possibility of internal relations between

separate personalities is denied. There follows an actual diminish-
ment of personality. For it is a fundamental and hence paradoxi-
cal truth that, the more isolate a man becomes as a self-centered
being distinct from all others, the less does he possess of a distinctively human personality. To define individual liberty altogether in terms of independence, as we Americans have been
inclined to do (from the first we've considered liberty to be the
product of a continuing "War for Independence")—to do this is to
ignore, and dangerously, a vital element of human freedom. It is
to deny the group life which each man requires for his fullest self-
expression, and it may well lead him at last into those wholly
irrational crowd-excitements which totalitarian dictatorships find
so useful to their purposes. This is not to say that independence is
no major element of human freedom; it certainly is; but there is
also in freedom a large measure of *de*pendence, and it is the de-
pendent element (that part of human nature so well satisfied, apparently, in the feudal society of the thirteenth century, though at
an excessive cost in terms of free speech and free inquiry) which
our schools have neglected. In all this our schools both express
and perpetuate that complex of attitudes and values and methods
of doing things which we call the "American Way of Life" and
which seems to be hostile, in several essentials, to organic river-
thinking. At its base seems to lie the assumption that the universe
is not really One but Many; that it is made up of bits and pieces
which are static in themselves, moved only from the outside; and
that whatever seems to flow through it or to indicate a fundamental organic unity is an illusion dangerous to "democracy."

Third, as community is lost the pressures toward neutrality
of mind and conformity of taste and conduct grow stronger;
tolerance becomes a purely negative virtue as our schools exem-
plify our society at large by dealing with minds as though they
were bodies (the brain but another muscle) and ideas as though
they were units of physical force. Students and teachers alike,

discouraged from a critical evaluation of society and of themselves as members of it, often give a virtually blind support to the political and economic status quo save where it happens to conflict with their private interests. Perhaps one cause of this is the fact that neutrality of mind *is* a prime virtue in the laboratory, where one dare not risk distorting sense-data with one's desires, aesthetic values, or moral judgments. In so far as this limited kind of scientific outlook prevails over all others, there is a tendency to regard as "real" only that schematic outline of reality which is the "natural world" of the physicist—colorless, odorless, soundless, valueless. All spirit, all emotion are thus ruled out in favor of abstract intellectualism. Means are divorced from ends (the atomic physicist, for example, is not concerned *as* physicist with the ends his work is to serve, nor is the engineer *as* engineer concerned with the human effects of the dam he builds). And factual information rather than living wisdom is deemed the proper aim of education. Any education dominated by such an outlook lacks vital substance. But I'm convinced that an even more important cause of this cult of neutrality (which is often mistaken for a genuine objectivity) derives from specialization. One effect of specialization has been the increased absorption of the individual by his economic function, so that his life becomes almost wholly organized around increasingly narrow selfish interests. These become the chief determinants of his public actions; his so-called "ideas" may be but flat reflections of them. Now an opposition of rational judgments may be resolved through argument, in which tests of consistency and of reference to external fact are employed; but an opposition of interests can be resolved in the last analysis only on the basis of that naked force which seems to be the ultimate consequence of all "pure" pragmatism. Obviously a publicly supported educational system cannot encourage one such interest against another until it is certain which interest is the more powerful. . . .

These three effects, I say, are disastrous to river-thinking. If we had deliberately set out to devise an educational system which would prevent wisdom in the handling of watershed problems, we could hardly have done so more effectively.

2

Example: Our Response to the Crisis of '51   Much of what I've tried to say here was exemplified, I think, in the response made by my home town, and by the college, to the flood crisis of 1951.

Even while that flood was upon us I was struck by the schism between body and mind which seemed evident in this response. I've spoken of the generosity which then marked our mood, but I must now add that our kindness of heart seemed to operate only if its objects were concretely present. The capacity for generalizing our emotion in terms of the situation which had evoked it, then refining it through rigorous logic into an abstract value by which flood-control proposals might be graded—this capacity seemed almost wholly absent. I remarked what seemed to me a significant disparity of quality between our response as bodies and our response as minds, the former being wholly admirable, the latter almost contemptible—for I thought that in our total response we showed ourselves to be physically courageous and energetic while remaining intellectually lazy and timid. Typical of the immediate reaction of some of the more vociferous among our local flood-control "experts" was the lead editorial published in the Kansas City *Star* during the last week of July 1951. Entitled "Build Now and Argue Later," it opened with the sentence, "Arguing theory is fine in its time and place, but the thing, now, is action." The closing sentence was, "Let's concentrate on flood control now and argue other methods or theories later"—thus blandly assuming that what was done on flood control had no

integral relation to what was done concerning irrigation, navigation, power development, and other aspects of the river's problem.

Particularly significant was the role played by Kansas State
itself, not only in the immediate crisis but also in long-term valley
developments.

The college's physical response to the challenge was superb.
Beautifully organized and administered under great pressure were
the housing and feeding of the 2,000-odd refugees, the supplying
of power to the stricken city, the emergency health and sanitation
programs, the recreational program so important to the maintenance of morale, and the communications network through which
co-ordinated effort became possible. College staff members, then
and later, worked to the limits of their physical strength on the
huge job of "digging out" and "fixing up" as the waters receded.

But what of the mental response? It was much more sluggish,
it was even reluctant, because it had to be made against inertia.
It required an actual reversal of college policy.

Now a man from Mars might find this fact astounding. Here
was the leading agricultural and engineering school of the Kansas
Basin and as such must, he might think, become a rational center
and disinterested critic of long-term basin programs. He might
expect the college's professors to have become by 1951 leaders of
public thought on such matters as conservation, irrigation, power
development, flood control, pollution abatement, and so on—
matters within the fields of their special competency. He might
expect that as citizens especially qualified by technical knowledge
they'd be outspoken in praise or blame of the work being done
and the proposals made for future work. He might expect the
college's Extension Service to have long conducted forums, pro-
moted lectures, provided information materials, distributed films,
and used all other legitimate devices for adult education in what
was, by all odds, the most important issue peculiar to this region.
The expected result by 1951 would be a considerable body of

enlightened public opinion on matters with which the present essays are concerned.

Nothing of the sort had happened.

A few, a very few, college staff members had in the past spoken out in public on one side or the other of the issue raised by the Army Engineers' big dam program, but these were quickly persuaded to shut up. One professor of engineering was warned by a Chamber of Commerce official that if he persisted in expressing publicly his strongly negative opinions of the Engineers and their work he'd lose his job. Nor did these pressures toward a mindless, spineless conformity originate wholly outside the college. The college administration had joined in them. On one occasion the college's information services and personnel were advised by an administrative officer to stay clear of the Tuttle Creek controversy because the institution might otherwise "get into trouble." Even while the flood was at its height, on a campus crowded with flood refugees, the college's council of deans was warning the president to go slow in planning an information and education program for valley development that might capitalize on the immense interest in this subject aroused by the catastrophe. The college, though an educational institution, had thus joined in a strategy of anti-education on public affairs, a strategy which had helped to keep us ignorant, timorous, and wholly unequipped to think straight on the basis of accurate information about issues which we—not merely those special interests with private axes to grind— should decide.

It seems to me obvious that the conception of ideas as simply rationalized interests, referred to on pages 204 and 205, was what had shut off the needed discussion. . . .

But if Kansas State be deemed a symptomatic institution, there is basis for hope in the fact that the 1951 disaster did result in a complete reversal of college policy on this matter—and with gratifying results. In late November of that year, upon the initiative of President James A. McCain, the college conducted on its campus a three-day forum on flood control which may well become an event of historic importance as its hopeful consequences continue to be realized. Participating in it as speakers and discussion leaders were Colonel L. J. Lincoln of the Corps of Engineers; Gladwin E. Young of the Department of Agriculture; Richard G. Baumhoff, author and journalist on the staff of the St. Louis *Post-Dispatch;* Leslie A. Miller, former governor of Wyoming; Val Peterson, governor of Nebraska; Edward F. Arn, governor of Kansas; John Ise, famed professor of economics at Kansas University; and officials of the U. S. Geological Survey, the Weather Bureau, the Soil Conservation Service, the Bureau of Reclamation, and the Kansas League of Municipalities, as well as Kansas State faculty members. The sessions, attended by hundreds of people from all over Kansas, were as exciting as they were informative (particularly so was a rather heated exchange between Leslie Miller and Val Peterson); the proceedings were broadcast by radio and later published in pamphlet form, and with other material were used by organized discussion groups throughout the state. President McCain said that these activities would be but the beginning of a process whereby the whole state might become, in a sense, the campus of his institution, and there is small doubt that they have had their effect in the watershed legislation prepared in 1952 for presentation to the state legislature, and in the work of the Blue Valley Study Association.

Moreover, it was intended that this effort be joined with revisions in curricula whereby some of the causes for criticisms made in earlier pages of this book might be removed. In this, President McCain would be continuing work begun by his predecessor, Milton S. Eisenhower, who as head of the institution from 1943 to 1950 sought in various ways to reduce what he called the "walls of specialization."

3

The Organic Concept as a Guide to Curricular Changes   But
how may these "walls" best be reduced? What specific changes
are needed to develop minds that can deal successfully with our
Kansas Basin problems?

These are questions I'm not competent to answer, certainly—
but as I've thought about them I've found myself referring repeatedly to personal experiences with the Soil Conservation
Service a dozen years ago. The SCS, as we've seen, is a key Federal agency in every agricultural valley, and I sometimes believe I
discern in my experience with it the vague outline of the answers
we seek. In any case, for whatever it's worth, I'm going to close
with it.

In the late 1930s I was a recent graduate of Kansas State, employed by the SCS in the upper Mississippi Valley region. I was
an "information specialist." We were all specialists in that new
bureau, being graduates of schools of agriculture, forestry, and
engineering. This specialization of ours was a main source of our
troubles as we sought to develop an effective erosion-control
program for the farms of our region. We had soils specialists who
were supposed to know everything about soil types, fertilizers,
and the like. We had agronomists who were specialists in field
crops and pasture management. We had engineers who specialized in the design and construction of terraces, wing dams, gully-
control structures, and so on. We had foresters who specialized
in tree planting and wood-lot management. We had wildlife
specialists who sought to develop better conditions for fish and
game birds. We had agricultural economists who specialized in
farm management. We had all these—and we also had endless
and often heated arguments as to the proper scope and relative
efficacy of our various specialties. Thus our regional office re-

flected the chaos of curricula, the concentration on means to the virtual exclusion of ends, in the colleges we had attended; it portrayed in miniature that chaos of bureaucracy which the Inter-Agency Committee tries to hide in the Missouri Valley.

Painfully we had to re-educate ourselves as we came up hard against our job; we suffered mental anguish as we broke down the mental barriers imposed on us by our college training. For our job required that we deal with a natural process, not with a static entity neatly subdivided into segments that accorded with the courses in which we'd majored as undergraduates. Our technical training suggested that we begin with the particular and proceed toward the general in our solution of the soil-conservation problem. Had we followed this suggestion we'd have sent an engineer out onto a farm to plan what structures were needed; we'd have sent out an agronomist to plan the crop rotations and pasture improvements; we'd have sent out a soils man to measure lime and fertilizer needs, and so on through the list of our technicians. With all these separate plans at hand we should have been able to combine them into a single master plan for the farm as a whole. But we discovered at once that it didn't work that way: the logical implications of our education proved to be impracticable, thus indicating that the premises of that education were false. We quickly found that a piecemeal approach to the farm led to a chaotic farm plan whose parts failed to hang together, and one which was contradictory in many respects to the plans made for other similar farms. Unhappy practical experience taught us that the *general* truth we required could never be achieved through a simple mechanical combination of the *particular* truths which (we'd been taught) composed it. It was precisely the concept of wholeness—a continuous unbroken integrity—which was necessary to the success of our operations, and of course this could never be achieved by placing one specialized block against another like stones in an uncemented wall.

Practical success required that we *first* see the farm as a whole. Our initial step became the mapping of the whole farm, placing on that map such basic planning data as steepness of slopes, degree of erosion, soil type, and the use being made of each acre. It was only in terms of this total conception that our various and partial techniques became truly valuable, truly effective of our purpose. Before long we actually banished from our field organization charts the personnel classifications of "agronomist," "engineers," and so on, replacing these with the designation "conservationist." We insisted that every man, no matter what his college major had been, must think of himself *as* a conservationist who employed whatever specialized techniques were indicated by a comprehensive view of the land to which his work plan applied. Moreover, he must realize in practice that no plan which concentrated on the physical control of erosion without regard to the farmer's economic needs and desires would be applied. A true conservationist must be a farm economist as well as agronomist-forester-engineer. Only in headquarters offices did the SCS retain specialists designated as such, and these were regarded as a pool of experts to be drawn upon by field men, and as supervisors of those portions of field work which lay within their special competencies.

But even a comprehensive view of the farm as a physical and economic entity was too narrow for our purpose. Very few farms *were,* in actual fact, physical entities in the sense that natural boundaries separated them from their neighbors; generally speaking, their boundaries were legal fictions having no regard for natural watershed lines—and for them runoff water with its erosion debris had no more respect than it had for the assigned limits of our college specialties. Often in a steep watershed it was impossible to solve one farm's erosion problem in isolation from those of the neighboring farms above and below it. From a recognition of this fact arose the concept of the watershed of a small stream as the natural unit to work with in setting up SCS "demonstration" projects—projects which were show windows for the display of soil-conserving programs. And from this grew the idea of setting up soil-conservation districts coinciding with natural watersheds, each district to be a legal subdivision of the state government, with authority to employ conservationists, enter into co-operative agreements with state and Federal agencies, purchase equipment and materials, and even in extreme instances impose land-use regulations. The district idea brought us into realms which our colleges had marked off as "political science" and from which most of us, by the necessities of our technical training, had been excluded as undergraduates. Here we were brought with bruising force against the hard fact that most natural drainage areas of a size suitable for district organization cut across county and township lines; to set up a district on this natural basis therefore involved legal difficulties so great that the idea had at last to be drastically modified. Most agricultural states adopted the necessary enabling law, but most of the districts finally established were not on a watershed but on a county basis.[1]

Certainly all this indicates the practical necessity for curricular revisions in agricultural schools. Does it also suggest, if vaguely, the *kind* of revision which might be made?

If we took our cue from the SCS experience we might begin our curricular revision by defining, very carefully, a concept of the valley as a natural and historic process, involving not only soil and water and other natural resources but also people with their needs and desires. The conservation of our natural resources and the development of our humanity might thus be seen as a single total process which could provide the integrating theme of all our

[1] Of course the watershed idea remained a vital, persuasive one. In 1953 it was embodied in the watershed legislation for flood control sponsored by Glenn Stockwell and others, as mentioned in an earlier essay.

separate studies. Every particular subject of study would then be realized as an aspect of the total process—*not* an isolated thing, but an aspect. Conservation, broadly conceived, would provide a continuous substratum of meaning for such specialized courses as agronomy, dairy husbandry, animal husbandry, and soils science, just as soil and water are the continuous support of all plant and animal life. The artificially rigid boundaries which have divided one aspect of agriculture from another in our teaching would be broken down. Moreover, the various specialties would be clearly related to economics and sociology and politics, and through them to ethical philosophy, for almost every fundamental issue which now divides us in public affairs can be adequately stated in conservation terms. As a matter of fact, I wonder if a curriculum planned along these lines might not lead us to remove the "vs." from between many of our present oppositions (those of the Individual vs. the State, for example, or of Private Profit vs. the General Welfare), enabling us to make at last those "Higher Syntheses" whose achievement, in my opinion, is necessary to our survival as a free society.

Certainly a curriculum planned along these lines would remove the "vs." from between "technical" and "liberal" education, for within it the two would be fused in a single teaching-and-learning process. The aims of technical and liberal education would become a single total aim, since there would be involved in the curriculum as a whole, permeating and giving meaning to every part, an idea of the citizen as a free member of a community whose Good Life is the purpose of all our vocational techniques, all our economics, all our politics. Sheer technical competency would, I think, be increased—for surely the vital meaning of each technical course would be greatly enhanced for the student if it were taught in terms of economics, aesthetics, and ethics. Similarly, the courses in the so-called humanities would be given increased meaning for those interested in agriculture if they were taught in terms of concrete realities with which the agriculture student is at the outset familiar. The end product should be a person who can consider the ultimate general Truth as well as the immediate practical Utility of all propositions which come before him.

I speak here of a curriculum for schools of agriculture, for it is to this that the SCS experience most clearly applies—but it seems to me that the general outlines of the suggestion might apply equally well to curricula for schools of engineering, schools of medicine, and those portions of the various schools whose aim is the development of research scientists.

Graduates of our engineering schools who go into such agencies as the Bureau of Reclamation, the Corps of Engineers, and the Soil Conservation Service are soon advanced into positions where their sole concern is no longer with the designing and building of structures; they must also help make the policy which determines whether or not, and where, such structures should be built. If they make bad policy, as quite generally they do, that fact reflects the failure of our educational system to train them adequately for their jobs—and this despite the fact that the engineering curriculum is almost wholly devoted to vocational training. Surely the use of an integrating theme analogous to conservation—and perhaps the conservation theme itself—might be used to teach engineers not only how to build big dams but also how to decide, on social and ethical and economic grounds, if a big dam in a specific instance is the best solution.

Essentially the same thing in different terms may be said about the graduates of our schools of medicine, I think. Doctors are increasingly called upon to make public health policy, a task for which most of them seem to be woefully ill equipped, since they bring to it very primitive social ideas and an extremely narrow view of their private interests. Surely our schools of medicine, if their curricula were organized in terms of medicine's total purposes, would turn out men who talked less nonsense about "socialized medicine" whenever a public health insurance bill was proposed in the Congress—men who could themselves help design a bill which would satisfy our social needs while avoiding those pitfalls of bureaucracy into which professional politicians may otherwise lead us.

As regards the education of research scientists, the situation at first glance appears to be different. It appears that intense specialization is so essential to scientific research as to exclude the possibility of fusing research training with liberal education in the manner suggested above. Nevertheless, possibilities and perhaps even necessities along that line are revealed, I think, by a closer look at the nature of scientific research as it has developed in our time.

A few years ago I had occasion to review the history of agronomic research at Kansas State, focusing on the research which had developed immensely improved varieties of wheat. I was struck by the fact that wheat research—which had begun simply with the selection of high-yielding strains in fields of Turkey wheat—had proliferated until it involved not only agronomists but other specialists who, when the work began, had no notion of contributing directly to it: geneticists, plant pathologists, entomologists, milling engineers and laboratory technicians, cereal chemists, soils chemists, the chemists of plant nutrition. And the latter specialists are now becoming actively involved in realms of investigation which were formerly the exclusive property of physics, the realms of atomic energy—for radioactive tracers are being increasingly employed to study the ways in which plants eat, digest, and distribute the food they take from the soil. Thus agronomy and physics—formerly so widely separated—are now, in wheat research, becoming organically linked, joined together by a continuous chain of investigations.

There appears to be manifest here a fundamental truth of research, a truth common to all branches of it: namely, that if intense specialization is required for successful scientific investigation—and it *is* required, of course—an ever-closer co-operation of specialties is *equally* required. Indeed, the tendency is to go beyond co-operation toward actual integration. No longer is it possible to define science meaningfully in terms of the compartments set up at a more primitive stage of scientific development —the compartments of botany, agronomy, zoology, organic chemistry, inorganic chemistry, physics, and so on. Such precise compartmentalization was possible only when research concerned itself with the relatively superficial aspects of nature. It is as though science were a magic tree growing out of the air, downward from its leafy crown into the earth of reality. For as science probes ever more deeply toward the heart of things, its separate branches are pulled together to form the trunk of a tree whose roots plunge downward into what was formerly the exclusive ground of physics, the realm of ultimate matter—and physics itself becomes increasingly *meta*physical. Thus there is a real sense in which scientific specialization may be said to breed ultimately its opposite—if only it goes deep enough—for the more intense the specialization (if intensity means a penetration into depths), the more concerned the scientist becomes with those broad general principles underlying *all* specialties. In other words, a true research scientist in these latter days, these days of concern with the ultimates of nature, necessarily finds himself dealing sooner or later with the common denominators of all specialties.

It is of course precisely with these common denominators that liberal education is concerned. And we may again note that these common denominators are of the essence of the concept of organism, the concept to which we have been led by all our essays into river-thinking.